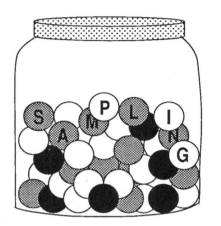

Statistics:
Prediction and
Sampling

A unit of study for grades 5–6
from USED NUMBERS: REAL DATA IN THE CLASSROOM

Developed at Technical Education Research Centers and Lesley College

Rebecca B. Corwin and Susan N. Friel

DALE SEYMOUR PUBLICATIONS

The *Used Numbers* materials were prepared with the support of National Science Foundation Grant No. MDR-8651649. Any opinions, findings, conclusions, or recommendations expressed in this publication are those of the authors and do not necessarily represent the views of the National Science Foundation. These materials shall be subject to a royalty-free, irrevocable, worldwide, nonexclusive license in the United States Government to reproduce, perform, translate, and otherwise use and to authorize others to use such materials for Government purposes.

Cover design and illustrations: Rachel Gage

Order number DS01037
ISBN 0-86651-516-X

DALE
SEYMOUR
PUBLICATIONS
P.O. BOX 10888
PALO ALTO, CA 94303

5 6 7 8 9 10 11-MA-95 94

USED NUMBERS STAFF

Co-principal investigators

Susan Jo Russell
Technical Education Research Centers (TERC)

Susan N. Friel
Lesley College

Curriculum development

Rebecca B. Corwin (TERC and Lesley College)
Tim Barclay (TERC)
Antonia Stone (Playing to Win)

Research and evaluation

Janice R. Mokros (TERC)
Alana Parkes (TERC)
Debra Gustafson (TERC)
John Olive (University of Georgia)
Deborah Ruff (University of Georgia)
Heide Wiegel (University of Georgia)
Bonnie Brownstein (Institute for Schools of the Future)
Ellen Bialo (Institute for Schools of the Future)
Michele Arsenault (Institute for Schools of the Future)
Mary Fullmer (University of Chicago)

Design and production

Elisabeth Roberts (TERC)
LeAnn Davis (TERC)
Jessica Goldberg (TERC)
John Abbe (TERC)
Edith Alvarenga (TERC)
Laurie Aragon (COMAP)

Cooperating classrooms for this unit

Dorothy Spahr
Wellesley Public Schools, Massachusetts

Barbara Fox
Cambridge Public Schools, Massachusetts

Reina Huerta
New York City Public Schools

John Wolfe
New York City Public Schools

Christine Fuentes
Clarke County Public Schools, Georgia

Diane Pearson
Clarke County Public Schools, Georgia

Advisory board

Joan Akers, California State Department of Education
Bonnie Brownstein, Institute for Schools of the Future
James Landwehr, AT&T Bell Laboratories
Steven Leinwand, Connecticut State Department of
    Education
John Olive, University of Georgia
David Pillemer, Wellesley College
Andee Rubin, Bolt Beranek and Newman Laboratories
Cindy Stephens, D. C. Heath
Marion Walter, University of Oregon
Virginia Wooley, Boston Museum of Science

Thanks also to advice and comment from Marilyn Burns,
Solomon A. Garfunkel (COMAP), and Bob Willcutt.

CONTENTS

PREFACE

In an information-rich society such as ours, statistics are an increasingly important aspect of daily life. We are constantly bombarded with information about everything around us. This wealth of data can become confusing, or it can help us make choices about our actions.

Educators and mathematicians now stress the importance of incorporating data analysis and statistics into the elementary mathematics curriculum to prepare students for living and working in a world filled with information based on data. The *Curriculum and Evaluation Standards for School Mathematics*, published by the National Council of Teachers of Mathematics in 1989, highlights statistics as one of the key content strands for all grade levels.

Many teachers see the need to support students in becoming better problem solvers in mathematics. However, it is difficult to find problems that give students the kind of experiences they need, are manageable in the classroom, and lead to the learning of essential mathematics. The area of data analysis—collecting, organizing, graphing, and interpreting data—provides a feasible, engaging context in which elementary grade students can do real mathematics. Students of all ages are interested in real data about themselves and the world around them.

Teaching statistics: Pedagogical issues

We introduce students to good literature in their early years. We do not reserve great literature until they are older—on the contrary, we encourage them to read it or we read it to them. Similarly, we can give young students experience with real mathematical processes rather than save the good mathematics for later.

Through collecting and analyzing real data, students encounter the uncertainty and intrigue of real mathematics. Mathematicians do not sit at desks doing isolated problems. Instead, they discuss, debate, and argue—building theories and collecting data to support them, working cooperatively (and sometimes competitively) to refine and develop such theories further.

Mathematicians and scientists use information or data like snapshots to look at, describe, and better understand the world. They cope with the real-world "messiness" of the data they encounter, which often do not lead to a single, clear answer.

Because statistics is an application of real mathematics skills, it provides the opportunity to model real mathematical behaviors. As students engage in the study of statistics, they, like scientists and statisticians, participate in:

▼ cooperative learning

▼ theory building

▼ discussing and defining terms and procedures

▼ working with messy data

▼ dealing with uncertainty

We want elementary school students to have the opportunity to engage in such real mathematical behavior, discussing, describing, challenging each other, and building theories about real-world phenomena based on their work.

Data analysis in the mathematics curriculum

Exploring data involves students directly in many aspects of mathematics. Data are collected through counting and measuring; they are sorted and classified; they are represented through graphs, pictures, tables, and charts. In summarizing and comparing data, students calculate, estimate, and choose appropriate units. In the primary grades, work with data is closely tied to the number relationships and measuring processes that students are learning. In the upper elementary grades, students encounter some of the approaches used in statistics for describing data and making inferences. Throughout the data analysis process, students make decisions about how to count and measure, what degree of accuracy is appropriate, and how much information is enough; they continually make connections between the numbers and what those numbers represent.

Instead of doing mathematics as an isolated set of skills unrelated to the world of reality, students can understand statistics as the vibrant study of the world in which they live, where numbers can tell them many different stories about aspects of their own lives. The computation they do is for a purpose, and the analysis they do helps them to understand how mathematics can function as a significant tool in describing, comparing, predicting, and making decisions. ■

TEACHING DATA ANALYSIS

The nature of data analysis

In data analysis, students use numbers to describe, compare, predict, and make decisions. When they analyze data, they search for patterns and attempt to understand what those patterns tell them about the phenomena the data represent.

A data analysis investigation generally includes recognizable phases:

▼ considering the problem

▼ collecting and recording data

▼ representing the data

▼ describing and interpreting the data

▼ developing hypotheses and theories based on the data

These phases often occur in a cycle: the development of a theory based on the data often leads to a new question, which may begin the data analysis cycle all over again.

Elementary students can collect, represent, and interpret real data. Although their work differs in many ways from that of adult statisticians, their processes are very

similar. Elementary school students can both analyze data and use those data to describe and make decisions about real situations.

Because real data are the basis for investigations in data analysis, there are no predetermined "answers." For example, if your class collects data on the ages of the students' siblings, the students understand that their job is more than simply coming up with an answer that you knew all along. Not only do you *not* know the answer in advance, but, without seeing the data, you may not even know what the most interesting questions are going to be!

While this situation encourages students to do their own mathematical thinking, it can also feel risky for you. Many teachers welcome a little uncertainty in their mathematics classes, when it prods their students to be more independent thinkers. To support you, the authors provide sample experiences from teachers who have used the activities described here so that you can be prepared for the kinds of issues that are likely to arise. You will soon build your own repertoire of experiences with data

analysis activities and will be able to anticipate likely questions, confusions, and opportunities.

The importance of discussion in mathematics

A central activity in data analysis is dialogue and discussion. While it is easy for you and your students to become engaged and enthusiastic in collecting data and making graphs, a significant amount of time should also be devoted to reflection about the meaning of the data.

Since students are not used to talking much during their mathematics work, it is important to support active decisionmaking by the students from the very beginning of the investigation. Students' participation in framing the initial question, choosing the methods of investigation, and deciding on ways to organize their data is essential. Once the data are collected and organized, the students must grapple with interpreting the results. If you have the outcome of a discussion or the "teaching points" you want to make too clearly in mind, you may guide students' observations too quickly into predetermined channels. When student ideas are ignored, misinterpreted, or rejected, they soon understand that their job is to second-guess the "answer" you had in mind.

On the other hand, if students find that *anything* they say is accepted in the same way, if every contribution is "a good idea" and no idea is ever challenged, they can lose motivation to participate. Ask students to reflect on, clarify, and extend their ideas and to listen to and ask questions of each other. Discussions in mathematics should encourage students to interpret numbers, make conjectures, develop theories, consider opposing views, and support their ideas with reasons.

Sensitive issues in data analysis

Students of all ages are interested in data about themselves and the issues they care about. Topics that matter enough to students to make them compelling topics for study often have very personal aspects. Investigations about families, heights, or students' chores, for example, can all bring up sensitive issues. After trying many topics in many classrooms, we have concluded that the potential sensitivity of a topic is not a reason to avoid it; on the contrary, these are the very topics that most engage student interest. All teachers deal with difficult or sensitive issues in their classroom, and the skills demanded of a teacher in handling issues that arise during data analysis activities are no different. Keep in mind that students may

sometimes want their data to be anonymous. Focusing on the patterns and shape of the class data, rather than on individual pieces of data, is particularly helpful, especially for upper elementary students.

Small-group work

Many of the investigations involve students working in teams. At first, keep small-group sessions short and focused. For students not used to working in small groups, assign specific tasks that encourage the participation of all the group members. For example, instead of, "Have a discussion in your group to decide what you want to ask the second graders about their bedtimes," you might say, "Come up with three possible questions you could ask the second graders."

The small-group activities provide an opportunity for your students to work in a cooperative setting. Depending on the amount of group work they have done before this unit, you may structure their group participation in a variety of ways. If they have not done much work in small groups, you may find yourself spending time in the first few sessions conveying clear expectations about their group work. If your students have a history of working in groups, this will be more automatic. It takes time to develop these skills, even when the group work is interesting and appealing.

The size of working groups is important; for this unit the most effective groups usually

have two or three (occasionally four) members. Larger groups seem to limit the participation of the quieter students. Find the size that works best to support good discussion and thoughtful listening.

As you plan your class sessions, think about how you want to group students for small-group work. You may want to establish groups for the entire unit, or create new groups for each investigation. Some teachers form groups randomly, using counting-off methods or by having students select numbers from a container. Others group students in order to mix personalities or other student attributes. Still others group by convenience (all those sitting near each other). However you decide to group, make sure your students are clear about their groups and their roles as group members.

Materials

Students need materials to represent their data during their investigations. These range from Unifix cubes to pencil and paper to computer software. What is most important is that students are able to construct multiple views of the data quickly and easily and that they do not become bogged down in drawing and coloring elaborate graphs (which are appropriate only at the very end of an investigation when students are ready to "publish" their findings).

Any material that can be moved easily and rearranged quickly offers possibilities for looking at data. For example, students might write or draw their data on *index cards* (or any paper rectangles); then these can be arranged and rearranged. *Unifix cubes* (or other interconnecting cubes) are another good material for making representations throughout the grades. We have found that *stick-on notes* (such as Post-it notes), with each note representing one piece of data, are an excellent material for making rough drafts of graphs. They can be moved around easily and adhere to tables, desks, paper, or the chalkboard. *Pencil and unlined paper* should always be available for tallies, line plots, and other quick sketch graphs.

Calculators

Calculators should be available, if possible, throughout the activities. Their use is specifically suggested in some of the investigations. It is no secret to students that calculators are readily available in the world and that adults use them often. But many students do not know how to use a calculator accurately, do not check their results for reasonableness, and do not make sensible choices about when to use a calculator. Only through using calculators with appropriate guidance in the context of real problems can they gain these skills.

Computers

Computers are a key tool in data analysis in the world outside of school. Graphing software, for example, enables scientists and statisticians to display large sets of data quickly and to construct multiple views of the data easily. Some software for the elementary grades allows this flexibility as well. A finished graph made by the computer may, for some students, be an appropriate illustration for a final report of their findings. But keep in mind that students also make interesting and creative graphs by hand that would not be possible with the software available to them. Other computer software, including software for sorting and classifying and data base software, is particularly useful for some data analysis investigations. Where the use of a software tool would particularly enhance a data analysis investigation, recommendations for incorporating its use are made in the text and noted at the beginning of the session.

Home-school connections

Many opportunities arise in data analysis investigations for communicating with parents about the work going on in the classroom and for including them as participants in your data investigations. When you begin this unit, you may want to send a note home to parents explaining that students will be studying data analysis in their mathematics class and that, from time to time, parents can be of assistance in helping students collect data from home. Parents or other family members often provide an available comparison group. Studies of age, family size, height, and so forth can be extended to include parents. If students are studying their own families, they may be interested in collecting comparison data about their parents' families. Including parents and other significant family members as participants in your data analysis investigations can stimulate their interest and enthusiasm for the work students are doing in school and, at the same time, help students see that the mathematics they do in school is connected to their life outside of school.

Interdisciplinary connections

Many teachers find ways to connect the data analysis experiences students have in mathematics to other areas of the curriculum. Data analysis is, after all, a tool for investigating phenomena of all kinds. The same approaches that students use in this unit can be called on for an investigation in science or social studies. Making these connections explicit and helping students transfer what they have learned here to new areas will give them an appreciation of the usefulness of mathematics throughout the curriculum. ■

STATISTICS: PREDICTION AND SAMPLING
UNIT OVERVIEW

Statistics: Prediction and Sampling is a unit of study that introduces students to using data collected from samples to make predictions. As the second of three upper-elementary units in the *Used Numbers* series, this unit has been designed for students in grades 5 and 6 who have had some experience in collecting, graphing, and interpreting data. *Statistics: Prediction and Sampling* builds on students' beginning data analysis experiences, particularly those introduced in *Statistics: The Shape of Data*. In *Statistics: Prediction and Sampling*, students:

▼ develop sampling plans to collect real data from a population

▼ represent collected data in a variety of ways

▼ describe landmarks and features of the data

▼ reason about relationships between samples and populations

▼ evaluate the representativeness of samples

▼ formulate hypotheses and build theories about the reality represented by the data.

How to use this unit

Like all the *Used Numbers* units, *Statistics: Prediction and Sampling* is organized into investigations that may extend from one to four class sessions. To cover the entire unit requires approximately 16 class sessions of about 45 minutes each. Teachers who have used this unit have found that a schedule of 2–3 sessions per week works best to maintain continuity while allowing enough time for reflection and consolidation between sessions. The activities are sequenced so that

students move gradually from more straightforward to more sustained investigations. The investigations are grouped into three parts:

▼ **Part 1: Introduction to sampling**

Sampling ourselves
How big is a family?
In the chips

▼ **Part 2: Using sampling**

Cats: Sampling a population of animals
Advertising decisions

▼ **Part 3: Solving problems with sampling**

Researching play injuries
A study of crime on television

The three parts work well as a single five-to-six-week unit. Some teachers have substituted this unit for textbook exercises on statistics or graphing. Others have used it toward the middle or end of the year to consolidate a variety of mathematical skills, because it brings together work in graphing, estimation, computation, and fractions or percents in a problem-solving context. The investigations on sampling are best done together as a cohesive unit. It is important that 2–3 sessions take place each week so that the experiences build on each other, allowing students gradually to develop and use their growing skills and understanding in the analysis of real data.

Planning the investigations

This guide gives you all the information you'll need to guide students through the investigations in *Statistics: Prediction and Sampling*. The information is organized as follows:

Investigation overview. This section includes (1) a summary of the student activity, (2) materials you will need for the investigation and any special arrangements you may need to make, and (3) a list of the important mathematical ideas you will be emphasizing. Plan to look carefully at this overview a day or two before launching the investigation.

Session activities. For each session, you will find step-by-step suggestions that outline the students' explorations and the teacher's role. Although suggestions for questions and instructions are given, you will of course modify what you say to reflect

your own style and the needs of your students. In all cases, the teacher's words are intended to be guidelines, *not* word-for-word scripts. Plan to read through this section before each session to get the general flow of the activities in your mind.

Dialogue Boxes. The Dialogue Boxes illustrate the special role of discussion in these investigations and convey the nature of typical student-teacher interactions. Examples are drawn from the actual experiences of classes that have used these investigations. They call attention to issues that are likely to arise, typical student confusions and difficulties, and ways in which you can guide and support students in their mathematical thinking. Plan to read the relevant Dialogue Boxes before each session to help prepare for interactions with your students.

Teacher Notes. These sections provide important information you will need about various mathematical concepts and data sets. Here you will find explanations of key aspects of the process of measuring and of collecting and analyzing data, including ways to graph data and how and when to introduce basic mathematical terms. The Teacher Notes are listed in the contents because many are useful as references throughout the unit, not just where they first appear. You might plan to read them all for background information before starting the unit, then review them as needed when they come up in particular investigations.

Goals for students

The "Important mathematical ideas" listed in the investigation overviews highlight the particular student goals for those sessions. The major goals for *Statistics: Prediction and Sampling* are as follows:

Part 1: Introduction to sampling

Describing the shape of the data in a sample. Students describe the results of their sampling activities by referring to a variety of features of the data ("The data ranged between 2 and 7") and the overall shape of the data distribution ("Most of us have between 3 and 5 people in our families").

Understanding relationships between populations and samples. In these first three investigations, students explore different kinds of populations. They also investigate the nature of samples and develop ideas about representativeness, selection, and size. Formal rules are not taught, but students do develop intuitive and effective ways of discussing the relationships between populations and samples.

Comparing the results of repeated samples of the same population. Students explore one population by taking repeated samples of the same size and find that the results of repeated samples can be different. Through this they learn that sampling cannot lead to exact answers, but that it provides a way of understanding the approximate distribution of data in a population.

Describing and analyzing sample data and inferring the nature of a population. Students develop and share techniques for extrapolating from sample data to an entire population. Various methods and models are supported through classroom discussion, small group work, and teacher instruction.

Part 2: Using sampling

Evaluating the representativeness of a sample. Whether a sample indeed represents a population is a central notion in statistics. Students begin with intuitive ideas about the "fairness" of samples, refining and developing those ideas through discussion, challenging each others' theories, and describing and defending their own.

Defining a question and developing a sampling plan. Students experience real-world statistical processes as they refine questions for their own research and develop sampling plans to investigate those questions.

Drawing conclusions about a population based on the results of sampling. Student investigations focus on taking the results of a sample and developing conclusions about the population from which the sample is drawn. After those conclusions are reached, students make decisions about actions that could be taken based on their knowledge about the population.

Part 3: Solving problems with sampling

Experiencing all the phases of a data analysis investigation in which sampling is used to collect data. Parallel to the phases of the writing process, a data analysis investigation includes "brainstorming" or discussion and definition of data collection methods; rough draft graphs of preliminary results; analyses leading to refinement of ideas, and final "publication" through reports of results. The final projects in this unit give students a chance to experience all phases of this process. ■

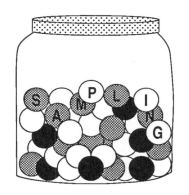

Statistics:
Prediction and
Sampling

PART 1
Introduction to sampling

SAMPLING OURSELVES

INVESTIGATION OVERVIEW

What happens

Small groups of students are selected as samples to represent the population of the class. The class collects information about a given characteristic from a sample group of students, describes the distribution, and then decides how well the information from the sample describes the class. Different methods for selecting members and different sizes of samples are tried. Students consider what happens when they make predictions about the whole class using limited information that they have gathered from samples.

Students then use the whole class as a sample of children in our society and collect data to compare with "official" figures. They evaluate whether they are a representative sample of the specified population.

The activities take three class sessions of about 45 to 50 minutes each.

What to plan ahead of time

▼ Duplicate Student Sheet 1 (page 89) for each small group of four students (Session 2).

▼ Think of one or two ways of biasing and randomizing small samples of the class (Session 1). For more information, see the Teacher Note, *Taking a sample*, (page 17).

Important mathematical ideas

Collecting and recording data. Students record data on line plots, a form of sketch graph that provides a convenient, quick picture of the distribution of numerical data.

Describing a population by taking samples. Although the population of an elementary school class is small enough to be surveyed without the use of samples, the point of this activity is to demonstrate that sometimes a sample is representative and sometimes it doesn't seem very representative of the population from which it is drawn.

Understanding that a sample may be too small or too big. Samples that are too small can fail to represent a population adequately, and samples that are too big may not save much time over doing a complete census. Students will be developing their informal ideas that the size of a sample can make a difference in how well it represents the population. At this level, they do not need to know precise formulas for finding the "right" sample size.

Reasoning from a sample to the population. Inferential reasoning is the focus of the entire module. Students have many different methods for making inferences from samples about the populations they represent. Some students picture the data distribution and construct a population with a similar distribution. ("There are a lot more at 6. It sticks up way higher. So I made the population look the same way.") Others work with percentages or proportions of samples. ("There are about two-thirds of us with brown eyes. I figure that if we are a sample of all the kids in the school, and there are 600 kids, then about 400 will have brown eyes.") Still others work numerically. ("If 15 out of 34 are red, then out of 100 it would be about three times as much, so that's about 45.") Encourage them to share their reasoning. Thinking about data is difficult, and sharing ideas allows students to pick a "best method" from a variety of approaches and models.

Talking about mathematical plans and outcomes. Talking about mathematical ideas is crucially important to understanding mathematical concepts and procedures. In these first sessions, students begin to talk with each other about mathematical issues. These student-to-student discussions need careful teacher support. ■

SESSION 1 ACTIVITIES

Introducing the unit

As part of our mathematics program and our study of statistics, we are going to learn about a special way of collecting data, called "sampling a population." What does it mean to take a sample of something?

Brainstorm a list of samples with the students ("Trying out my friend's shampoo"; "Asking five kids I know if they liked a certain movie"; "When they ask you who you're going to vote for"). Try to include items that do not involve opinion surveys, such as samples chosen for medical research, or samples that are selected and measured or weighed or counted, and not determined by asking questions. For example, students may be familiar with the biological research that uses sampling to identify and estimate animal populations.

Once students have generated a fairly long list, ask them what all the items have in common. Allow time for them to reflect on the similarities and to generalize: What's a sample for? Emphasize the idea of using a sample as a way to gather information about a larger group, which we call a *population*.

Be sure students see that samples are chosen to help someone make decisions about the "whole" population—the whale population, the incidence of disease in a group, whether people thought the TV show was worth watching, or the way the town is likely to vote in the next election. For an example of this class discussion, see the Dialogue Box, *Introducing sampling to upper elementary students* (page 16), and for background information, see the Teacher Note, *Sampling, populations, and prediction,* (page 16).

Can samples ever give us wrong information? If they aren't always exactly right, what use are they? Why take samples?

You are going to learn about taking samples and how samples can help you describe and analyze data. This is a part of the study of statistics. The questions we'll be exploring are how and when samples are useful, and how the data collected from samples can be used to find out information and make decisions.

The Teacher Note, *Taking a sample* (page 17) provides additional background information about sampling.

Let's do some sampling now to get the flavor of what you'll be studying in the next few weeks.

Exploring the sampling process: Sampling ourselves

Samples are used when the population is too big to count. When we want to know something about the whole town, or maybe about everyone in the United States, there are ways that mathematicians take samples, analyze them, and then make informed predictions about the population in question.

We're going to use our class as a population to see how sampling works. For a minute, let's suppose that we can't count the class and we don't know anything about it. Let's also pretend that only sample students can talk, but we want information about the whole class. Because we can't poll everyone, we're going to ask a sample of four students about something, and then infer from that sample what we think is true about how the class might respond to the same question. The first question we'll try to answer through sampling is, "What part of our class is right-handed?"

Select four students to be the sample group. Have these four students sit or stand together. Ask for a report about their dominant hand, and make a tally on the board. What's the general picture that emerges? (For example: [Most/all/few/half/ less than half] of the students in the sample are right-handed.)

Remember, we're pretending we can't ask all of you, so we have to go from this sample. Based on this sample of the class, what portion of the whole class would you predict to be right-handed? How could you figure this out?

Allow a little time for students to discuss their inferences and their methods. Then collect the "real" data from the class. Be sure to count the four who were in the sample—they are, after all, members of the population from which they were drawn. Display class results on the board alongside the data from

the sample; the data do not need to be formally organized—a simple table will probably do quite well. Ask students to compare the "real" outcome with their predictions.

What can you say in general about the class data? How does it compare with the results from the sample? How well did the sample provide representative information about the class?

A sample of four is quite small. It may well be too small to be representative. Select a different sample of eight students and ask the same question again. Does this result get closer to the "real" profile of the class?

What do you think would make a sample representative of a population? What factors should we look for?

Select a different sample of four students and ask a new question, "Do you walk to school?" Have students analyze the results of the sample survey. What can they say about the sample results? What would they expect of the whole class?

Before you ask the whole class for their data, send the sample of four back to the whole group and choose a new sample of eight students to respond to the question. Again, ask the class to respond to the results, and to extrapolate to the whole class. Are the results similar each time? Are they reasonable?

Collect the whole-class data—how many walk to school?—and ask them to compare

the actual data with their predictions. Did the samples adequately predict the whole-class results? Does a larger sample seem more representative?

As a final sample, and to show the students that samples can be less than representative, ask the question, "What color eyes are typical of our class?" Stack the deck by selecting a sample of all brown-eyed or all blue-eyed students, or a mixed sample whose proportion is not typical of the class. Your students may well start complaining about "fairness" even before you ask them whether this sample is representative.

Collect the data and ask students to infer from the sample. Then collect data from the entire class. When the whole-class results are quite different, ask them why they think that happened. This would be a good place to introduce the idea of the representativeness of a sample. A sample should be selected so that it is representative of the population. Certainly a teacher who selects students with certain characteristics is biasing the samples. See the Teacher note, *Taking a sample* (page 17), for more information.

As you learn more about sampling, you will be taking samples from different populations and trying to describe the population using the information you gather. At first you can "check" with the "real" populations to see if your samples are truly representative, but you won't always be able to do this. ∎

Introducing sampling to upper elementary students

This fifth grade teacher is introducing her class to the study of sampling as part of their work in statistics. As students offer their ideas of what sampling means, she lists them on the board.

You have already spent some time collecting data and talking about it in another unit. We're going to be starting something new today—a statistical procedure called sampling. When I say "sample," what do you think of?

TIM: A lemonade stand where you taste different things.

GREG: A freebie.

Why is it free?

GREG: They want you to buy it!

Who else has an idea about samples?

BETTINA: When they have sales at the store they talk about sample sizes. Is that the same?

MANUEL: On television they tell you that they took a sample of all the people in the United States and a bunch of them think a certain way.

MARGOT: When they talk about testing new medicines, they have to take samples of people's blood and stuff so they know that they're OK.

[After more ideas come up, and the list on the board is quite long] . . .

Look at our list and see if you can put into words what sampling is, or what a sample means, or what these things have in common.

MARIAN: A sample is like a little piece of something like your blood or like a group of people or something and it's like used to tell about the rest of the thing.

EMILIO: It's a part of something. Like a sample of air from my basement.

Yes, for a radon test. Why would people take a sample of something?

ISAAC: It's too hard to get the whole thing. Like whales, you know. You can't see them because they're under the ocean and you can't tell they're there. So you have to count the ones that show. Like on TV.

☞ These students had a lot of prior knowledge that began to come out as they talked more and more. Their knowledge allowed them to begin to formulate a working definition of sampling, which will be helpful in all their work on this unit. The teacher played a very low-key role in the discussion, clarifying an idea here and there, but mostly recording suggestions and then posing questions designed to help students synthesize their ideas. ■

✎ TEACHER NOTE
Samples, populations, and predictions

Taking samples is helpful when we really can't count all the people, or see all the animals, or interview everyone before the election. When the population is too large or too distant or too dense to count, samples help us approximate the population.

Statistical sampling procedures are used in all fields of science. Scientists who study whales use statistics (i.e., the number of whales sighted in a season) to tell whether the whale population is growing or shrinking. Public health officials keep track of the numbers and locations of disease outbreaks in the country and use statistics to locate and measure the size of epidemics.

You may be able to find a local business-person who uses inferential statistics at work. An insurance company, a fast-food franchise, or a large grocer may use sampling to make up their orders or to determine their rates. Inferential statistics involves taking a sample of a population and making inferences, or predictions, about the population, using the results from the sample.

The terms "population" and "sample" are precise statistical terms. One goal of this unit is to have students understand these terms and the relationships between samples and the populations they are drawn from.

A **sample** is a subset of a population; it is chosen (often randomly) in order to provide information about the population of which items in the sample are members. Thus a fifth grade class is a sample of all the fifth graders in your town; every tenth person entering a store is a sample of the shoppers in the store at that particular time; the so-called "Nielsen" families are a sample of all television viewers in the United States. Objects can be sampled, too. Every fiftieth computer chip may be pulled from an assembly line and inspected; similarly, every hundredth box of raisins may be weighed on its way out of the factory. Samples can be taken from most populations.

The **population** is the whole group you are studying. It may be a group of people or a group of animals or candies. You may or may not know the total number of members of the population. The inexact nature of sampling is frustrating to people who want to know "for sure." There are many situations in which there is no way to find an exact answer. For this reason, statistics is sometimes called a science of dealing with uncertainty. The first three investigations in this module provide opportunities for your students to compare their sample results directly with detailed information about the whole population. This is atypical of sampling, but it demonstrate clearly how sampling works. After those first sessions, we assume that an appropriately selected sample or series of samples provides representative information about the population. With real surveys, there are seldom any opportunities to "check" the results, although certainly the results of an election offer the chance to check pre-voting day predictions.

Samples are evaluated on many criteria, but two predominate. One is sample **size** and the other is the **method of selection.** Both affect how representative the sample is. If, for instance, you are trying to find out about pierced ears and your sample is all boys, you may get different results than if your sample includes the same number of boys and girls. It's easy to see why the number in a sample is important; gathering information from a sample of 2 students is very different from using a sample of 10 students.

The overall goal of students should be to get experience in **sampling,** rather than to find out in every case "whether we were right." Making sensible decisions is very important in statistical studies, but "being right" is not a reasonable goal; *being sensible* is a reasonable goal. Class discussions will be most fruitful if the focus is kept on the relationship between the sample and the population—the size of the sample and how well the sample represents the population.

Are students moving sensibly between sample results and claims about the population? Are they continuing to assess the representativeness of their samples? Can they evaluate their sampling plans and come up with modifications if they believe them to be needed? ■

✎ TEACHER NOTE
Taking a sample

Researchers don't always take a sample of a population in order to draw conclusions. Sometimes a census, or a complete count of the population, is a reasonable way to answer their questions.

Normally, however, it's too hard to count everyone in a population. For that reason, a manageable-sized group is selected as a sample. There are mathematical formulas that determine the "right size" for a sample, and there are special procedures that are often followed to assure that a sample is indeed a representation. A sample should be like a good magnifying mirror, reflecting back the details of the image without distorting it.

For example, the people who design standardized tests for elementary schools don't collect complete data from every fifth grader in the country when they decide what a "fifth grade" level score is. That would be too clumsy, and by the time the data were sorted and analyzed, it would be too expensive. Testmakers select samples and administer their tests to those samples of the population.

Many samples are **biased,** and that bias affects their representativeness of a population. Looking at housing prices for New England will not yield representative data for the whole country. Likewise, data gathered only from voters registered in one party will not represent all who will vote in an election; some registered voters will not participate, and some voters cross party lines.

A biased sample is not reflective of a population. When you work with samples you may be able to bias your class samples by selecting all left-handed students or all of one eye color or all of one gender. The traditional way around such a problem is to **randomize** samples.

Random samples can be selected through a variety of methods, such as rolling dice, or pulling names out of a hat, or using the telephone book. Each member of the population has an equal chance of being in the sample. At other, times, **stratified** samples are more appropriate. Parts of the sample are chosen from each of several clusters or groups; for example, classes, grade levels, or different geographic areas.

Sometimes **convenience** samples are used. In that case, researchers may not have a carefully randomized sampling plan, but may decide to ask the people they can contact fairly simply—for example, by interviewing their friends, or the people who have the same lunch hour. A case can be made for why these samples may represent a population fairly well, but there's always a danger that researchers who use convenience samples may not be taking representative samples.

There are many, many other ways of taking samples. Your students might want to explore this further and read more about researchers who use sampling as part of their ongoing work. ■

SESSION 2 ACTIVITIES

Exploring the sampling process

Today we are going to continue taking samples of our class, and we will look at the way different samples can lead to different conclusions. You will work in groups of four, treating yourselves as a sample of the population of the class. There are four questions to research. You will make predictions about the population based on your sample information. I'll give you a list of the questions you'll ask about your small group. Take about ten minutes to sample yourselves and make predictions; then we'll compare notes.

Divide the class into groups of four and distribute copies of Student Sheet 1, *Some questions to ask*. As you circulate, help students understand that they are to make predictions about the class from their sample alone. Continue to pretend that no one has access to whole-class information.

Each sample group answers the questions, compiles their small-group results, and then makes predictions or inferences about the class based on their sample results. There is space on the paper to record their inferences.

Talking it over: Sharing results

Call the whole class together to discuss their samples and predictions. You may want to assign a spokesperson from each group to respond. It works well to take this question by question and to record each small group's data on the chalkboard.

For the first question, compile the data for the whole class and see whether the samples were generally accurate. If a sample was not a good predictor, ask students why they think that might have happened. These samples are small ones, and they may not reflect the whole class very well.

Proceed through each question, looking at the similarities and differences among the small-group results and the whole-class data. Students may notice that the sample is more similar to the class's data when the data are more uniform—if no one has a baby sister, or if everyone is allowed to stay up after 11:00 PM on weeknights.

When the small-group and whole-class data have been compared for all four questions, review by asking students again what factors they believe affect the representativeness of their samples.

Developing a sampling plan for the class: Trying out student questions

Researchers who know they will be using a sample need to develop a procedure or a plan for choosing that sample. Let's see if we have enough knowledge now to make our own plan for sampling our class. Let's say I wanted to find out whether you thought you should be allowed to [eat during class time]. *(Pick some*

rule you think most students will have strong feelings about.) **In finding this out, I want to save myself time and just ask a sample of you. How could I pick a sample that would be representative of the whole class?**

Developing a simple sampling plan can be enjoyable. See the Dialogue Box, *What's a sampling plan?* (page 20). Support students' ideas about a plan for the class. As they make suggestions, ask for their reasons and help them think through the issues of representativeness that they are now wrestling with. How can they pick a fair, representative sample of the class? Should they draw straws? Roll dice? And how many of them should participate to make it fair?

When the class has agreed on a sampling plan, test it with a question that your students suggest.

Let's try out your sampling plan, and see how the results compare with real whole-class data. Who has a question to suggest? First, we'll select a sample of the class following your new sampling plan. Then we'll ask them the question, record their results, and make our prediction.

Follow through until you have a prediction about the class as a population. Then have everyone answer the question, and compare the whole-class data with your predicted results from the sample.

Evaluate the results of the chosen sampling plan with the students. Does it seem to be

representative of the class? Why or why not?

Extensions

Some students may want to keep taking surveys of the class by selecting samples and polling them. Suggest that anyone who is interested can keep working on the issue of the sampling plan; others may want to do repeated surveys of the class on a variety of issues.

If your sampling plan seems viable and you enjoy drama in your teaching, you might try "sudden sampling" during the next few days. Maybe there's an item in the news; perhaps something happens in the community. You could mimic the tone of the "Roving Reporter" who interviews people on the street, and call the sampling plan into action. One teacher even went so far as to assign a new classroom job—that of the Sampling Monitor, who administered the sampling procedures whenever there was an issue that needed to be resolved quickly. Be careful about when you use sampling, though! Students prefer voting on issues they care strongly about. There are some good lessons in that discovery. ∎

""DIALOGUE BOX
What's a sampling plan?

The students in this fifth grade class had decided that they would try to figure out whether their schoolmates were in favor of being able to eat snacks during class time. Using themselves as a sample, they found out that 13 of them did want to be able to eat snacks during class, and 15 didn't.

Their teacher made sure that they knew that an opinion survey would not necessarily mean that school policy would be changed. Then she suggested they try to figure out how the rest of the school felt. The students set out to develop their sampling plan before taking any action. There were four classes at each grade level from 1-6, making 24 classes, plus 4 kindergarten classes.

What do you think we should do about taking samples?

RICHARD: Let's ask everyone so we can be sure.

KIMBERLEY: No, that's silly. We'd have to ask lots too many kids and it would be a waste of time. We should ask some kids and use them as a sample of the whole school.

Should you ask the kindergarteners?

BEVERLY: No. They're too young to know.

MARY LOU: They aren't too young. I used to get real hungry in kindergarten and Miss

Schmidt made us wait too long.

JOSEF: I agree with Mary Lou. We need to ask everyone.

BEVERLY: But what about how messy the kindergarteners are? If they ate during classes they'd make a mess.

MARY LOU: We might too. We don't know how it would be for sure.

Well, what sample of the whole school shall we take?

GREG: One thing we could do is only take one class for each grade level. Then we would only have to ask in six rooms and we'd know enough from that.

Does it matter if the students all come from one classroom?

ISAAC: Maybe it could. Maybe we could get around that.

BETTINA: What if we went out to recess when just the third graders were out and we asked 25 of them?

EMILIO: No, I don't think that's good. Maybe they'd be the kids who were just standing around and not playing and maybe they'd be different from the kids who were playing games.

KELLEY: We could take some from each classroom. Can we get a list of the kids in a room and then choose them?

How would you like to choose them?

KELLEY: We could pick names out of a hat or

something.

So how many would you take from each room?

SARAH: I think maybe 6 or 7. That would give us 24 or 28 from each grade, and that's about a fourth. I think that's enough.

That sounds workable. Let me ask a question, though. Do you think it matters if they're evenly spread in the grades?

YOLANDA: I think yes because we don't know and we need to see if the sixth graders are maybe different from the first graders. Because if one grade really doesn't want it, they can stay like now.

Remember, no promises about change!

[*General response: Yeah, OK, Oh, yeah.*]

And then how will we decide who asks questions? And what do they ask? And how do they keep track?

BETTINA: We already know what to ask, because we asked ourselves.

Was the question clear enough? Could some-one who didn't help write it know what it was about?

[*General agreement that it was clear enough.*]

ISAAC: Can we just each take a class? I mean each three of us.

Does that seem reasonable?

SARAH: Well, three of us can do a good job because we can ask 2 kids each. That won't take too long and we can keep track because it's not too many.

JOSEF: But wait a second. If we have to ask 6 kids in a class and four classes, then we need four groups at each grade, and that's 24 groups. And we don't have that many. We only have nine.

[*The students wrestled with the arithmetic until they decided that they would split into pairs, and each pair would be responsible for two classrooms, or 12 students. The next day the teacher provided them with class lists for the classes they were to ask, and they selected the 6 target students by drawing names.*]

☞ Here the teacher is willing to let the students decide on a representative sample. She raises issues about making choices, and reminds students of the decisions they must make, but she is not shaping the decisions. The discussion went on until a plan was developed, the students understood it, and they were ready to conduct their survey. ∎

SESSION 3 ACTIVITIES

Introducing the problem: How old were you when you got your first watch?

Today, instead of using the class as a population, we're going to use the whole class as a sample of the population of schoolchildren in our country. First, we'll collect some data about our class. Then we'll look at some national figures and talk about similarities and differences.

We're going to collect data on the question, "How old were you when you got your first watch?"

Organizing and displaying data: Line plots

As they collect the data on this question, students might make a data display directly on the chalkboard with a line plot, or they may want to organize their data in a table first. See the Teacher Note, *Line plot: A quick way to show the shape of the data* (page 23). Whatever approach you choose, it should be done quickly. This data display is informal in nature—it is a tool for further analysis, not an end in itself.

Be sure to decide what to do about students who do not have and never have had watches. There must be a category for them. When the issue arises, be sure to handle it sensitively. Talking about the adults in the school environment who do not wear watches might help.

Describing the data: What's the shape of these data?

Looking at our data, what can we say about the age that class members typically were when they received their first watch?

Reflect with the class. Encourage students to look at and describe the overall shape of the data. (See the Teacher Note, *The shape of the data: Clumps, bumps, and holes*, page 23.) Ask about outliers, and encourage individuals to comment on what they can see— and what they *cannot* see— in the data. Are there any surprises? Interpreting such a display is the heart of descriptive statistics. For a sample discussion, see the Dialogue Box, *Describing the shape of the data* (page 24).

Comparing: Are our results like others?

What would you say if someone asked you how old a child in the United States is when he or she first gets a watch? Do our data help answer that question? (If this class is a sample, who would the population be?)

Write on the board the following statistic from the Timex Corporation: The average American received his or her first watch at age 6-1/2.* Ask students to compare their

*Timex Corporation, Waterbury, Connecticut, as cited in L.H. Lapham, M. Pollan, and E. Etheridge, *The Harper's Index Book* (New York: Holt, 1987).

results with the claim from the Timex Corporation and talk about similarities or differences.

After they have had time to react, encourage their informal explanations for the similarities or differences in results. Expect statements like these: "This isn't the same as everyone in the country because we didn't ask any adults. . . . We really don't have enough people in the sample. . . . It could be different in our class because we have [more/fewer] watches than they do. . . .What about people who don't have any watches?"

Upper elementary students often seem to know when a sample is not representative of a population, but supporting their instincts with evidence is difficult for some of them. Allow them time to express their reservations and their concerns, but recognize that they will not all be able to identify precisely the source of their discomfort. Some of your students will also have a good understanding that the size of the sample is a crucial issue, and they will be suspicious that their class is not large enough to represent "the average American."

The Timex Corporation is reported to have made that statement in 1986. If your students' data are very different, they might write a letter to the public relations department at Timex, reporting on their own watch data and contrasting them or comparing them with the statistic given in *The Harper's Index Book.*

Collecting more data: Comparing with other groups

Repeat the above activity, treating the class as a sample for one of these questions:

What percentage of American fifth graders report being in love? [*Answer: 39 percent*]

What percentage of American fifth graders report thinking a lot about hunger and poverty? [*Answer: 52 percent*]*

☛ Note that these data are for fifth graders. If your students are sixth graders, ask them what similarities or differences they would predict.

Because of the sensitive nature of these questions, you may find that the students would rather record their data secretly on paper to be passed directly to you.

Although it is tempting to use this lesson to teach percentage, it's better not to. Instead, stress estimation skills. That is, 39 percent is nearly 40 percent, which is four-tenths or two-fifths. A student might say, for instance, "Well, it's a little less than half of the population, and since we got 14 out of 31 kids in our class saying yes, then I think it's about the same." This demonstrates a good solid understanding of proportion. Ask different students to explain how they can

---

* The results for both questions are from the Search Institute, Minneapolis, as cited in L.H. Lapham, M. Pollan, and E. Etheridge, *The Harper's Index Book* (New York: Holt, 1987).

tell that the national and class percentages are about the same or quite different.

Whether or not their results are similar to those of the cited survey, ask your students if they believe they are a representative sample of all fifth graders in the country. (Again, if your class is not a fifth grade class, you may choose to use other data.) Who is *not* represented if your class is used as a sample?

Whether they are a rural, urban, or suburban population, students should recognize that they are not representative of the variety in the country. Are they ethnically diverse? Economically diverse?

What would you have to do to make a sampling plan for all of the fifth graders in the country?

Challenge your students with that task, which is a good extension activity for those who are interested. Perhaps they would like to write to the Search Institute to find out how their data were collected. What was their sample? How many kids? Chosen how? From where? Encourage anyone who is so inclined to follow up and make a report on the results.

As we continue our study of statistics, we will be collecting other data and looking at ways of analyzing a sampling plan for our community. We'll start with data collection from you, and then we'll go on to collect more data from a bigger sample. ■

TEACHER NOTE
Line plot: A quick way to show the shape of the data

A line plot is a quick way to organize numerical data. It clearly shows the range of the data and how the data are distributed over that range. Line plots work especially well for numerical data with a small range.

This representation is often used as a working graph during data analysis. It is an initial organizing tool for beginning work with a data set, *not* a careful, formal picture used to present the data to someone else. Therefore, it need not include a title, labels, or a vertical axis. A line plot is simply a sketch showing the values of the data along a horizontal axis and X's to mark the frequency of those values in the data set. For example, 18 students doing the investigation, *How big is a family?* have just collected data on the number of people in their families, and a line plot showing their data looks like this:

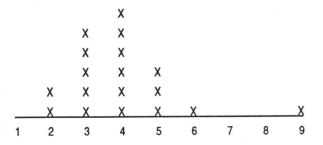

From this display, we can quickly see that nearly two-thirds of the students have families with either 3 or 4 members. Although the range is from 2 to 9, the interval in which most data fall is from about 3 to 4. The outlier, at 9, appears to be an unusual value, separated by a considerable gap from the rest of the data.

One advantage of a line plot is that we can record each piece of data directly as we collect it. To set up a line plot, start with an initial guess from students about what the range of the data is likely to be: What do you think the lowest number will be? How high should we go? Leave some room on each end of the line plot so that you can lengthen the line later if the range includes lower or higher values than you expected.

By quickly sketching data in line plots on the chalkboard, you provide a model of using visual displays to get a quick, clear picture of the shape of the data. ■

TEACHER NOTE
The shape of the data: Clumps, bumps, and holes

Describing and interpreting data is a skill that must be acquired. Too often, students simply read numbers or other information from a graph or table without any interpretation or understanding. It is easy for students to notice only isolated bits of information (e.g., "Vanilla got the most votes"; "Five people were 50 inches tall") without developing any overall sense of what the graph shows. Looking at individual numbers in a data set without looking for patterns and trends is something like decoding the individual words in a sentence without comprehending the meaning of the sentence.

To help students pay attention to the shape of the data—the patterns and special features of the data—we have found it useful to use such words as *clumps, clusters, bumps, gaps, holes, spread out, bunched together*, and so forth. Encourage students to use this casual language about shape to describe where most of the data are, where there are no data, and where there are isolated pieces of data.

A discussion of the shape of the data often breaks down into two stages. First, we decide what are the special features of the shape: Where are the clumps or clusters, the gaps, the outliers? Are the data spread out, or are lots of the data clustered around a few values? Second, we decide how we can interpret the shape of these data: Do we have theories or experience that might account for how the data are distributed?

As an example, consider the following sketch graph of the weights (in pounds) of 23 lions in U.S. zoos.

25–49	✔ ✔
50-74	
75–99	
100–124	✔ ✔
125–149	
150–174	
175–199	
200–224	✔
225–249	✔
250–274	
275–299	✔ ✔ ✔
300–324	✔ ✔ ✔
325–349	✔ ✔
350–374	✔
375–399	✔
400–424	✔ ✔ ✔
425–449	✔
450–474	✔ ✔ ✔

(Source: Zoos in Atlanta, Cleveland, Little Rock, Memphis, Miami, the Bronx, Philadelphia, Rochester, San Antonio, and Washington, DC. Data collected in 1987.)

In the first stage of discussion, students observed the following special features:

▼ There is a clump of lions between 400 and 475 pounds (about a third of the lions).

▼ There is another cluster centering around 300 pounds (another third).

▼ There are two pairs of much lighter lions, separated by a gap from the rest of the data.

In the second stage of discussion, students considered what might account for the shape of these data. They immediately theorized that the four lightest lions must be cubs. They were, in fact, one litter of 4-month-old cubs in the Miami Zoo. The other two clusters turned out to reflect the difference between the weights of adult male and female lions.

Throughout this unit, we strive to steer students away from merely reading or calculating numbers drawn from their data (e.g., the range was 23 to 48, the median was 90, the biggest height was 52 inches). These numbers are useful only when they are seen in the context of the overall shape and patterns of the data set and when they lead to questioning and theory-building. By focusing instead on the broader picture—the shape of the data—we discover what those data have to tell us about the world. ■

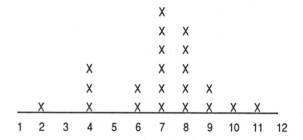

66,99 DIALOGUE BOX
Describing the shape of the data

These students have just found out the ages at which class members first received a wrist watch. They have recorded the data on a line plot and are beginning to talk about what they can see.

So what can you say about these watch data? Let's hear a few of your ideas.

BETTINA: Well, there are a lot at 7.

TIM: There was only one at 2 and one at 10 and one at 11.

ISAAC: There are two at 6 and 9.

What else do you notice?

JOSEF: Two is the youngest.

So no one in our class was given a watch before the age of 2?

MARY LOU: Yeah. And 11 was the highest.

So the range was from 2 to 11. What else?

ETHLYN: There's nothing at 5.

Ethlyn's noticing that there is a hole in this part of the data. Can anyone say any more about that?

GREG: There's nothing at 1 either.

Yes, 2 is the lowest count and there's nothing below it. But this situation, that Ethlyn noticed at 5, is a little different. What can you say about that?

BENJAMIN: Mostly, the ages cluster around 7 or 8, but sometimes you get something higher or lower.

Can anyone add to that?

MANUEL: You must have really nice parents if you got one when you were 2.

In fact, mathematicians have a name for a piece of data which is away from the rest of the data. They call it an *outlier*. An outlier is an unusual piece of data—sometimes it might actually be an error in the data, but sometimes it's just an unusual piece of data. It's usually interesting to try to find out more about an outlier. Who had the outlier in this case?

YOLANDA: I did. I know I was 2 because my sister had her first communion then and they didn't want me to cry, so they gave me a watch when they gave her one. Mine was a pretty junky one, but I loved it.

Any other stories about getting watches when you were young?

[*Later*] . . .

So if someone asked you, "What's the typical age when kids in this class got watches," what would you say?

MANUEL: Well, I'd say 7.

[*Addressing the class as a whole, not just the student who answered*] Why would 7 be a reasonable description of the age when students in our class first got watches?

BETTINA: Because most of us were 7.

MANUEL: I don't think so. There were six kids who were 7, but most of the kids got watches at a different age.

GREG: More kids got watches when they were 7 than any other age.

Any other ways to say this? Or any different ideas?

MARGOT: Well, I wouldn't say just 7.

Why not?

MARGOT: Well, there's really not that much difference between 7 and 8. They've got most of us all close together. I'd say 7 or 8 'cause the 6 or the 9 aren't what you'd usually get.

So Margot is saying she'd use an interval to describe the typical age of getting a watch in our classroom, from 7 to 8, and Manuel and Bettina said they'd say 7 was about the typical age. What do other people think about that?

☛ In this discussion, the class has moved gradually from describing individual features of the data to looking at the shape of the data as a whole. The teacher introduced the terms interval, *range*, and *outlier* because they came up in the discussion and were appropriate in describing these data. Throughout the conversation, the teacher tries to have students give reasons for their ideas and pushes them to think further by asking for additions or alternatives to ideas students have raised. ■

HOW BIG IS A FAMILY?

INVESTIGATION OVERVIEW

What happens

To find the typical family size for their class, students decide how to define family membership and then collect and represent class data. They compare their typical family size with that of the city or town where they live and consider the adequacy of themselves as a sample for that population. Students then collect more family-size data and explore how these new data change their predictions.

The activities take three class sessions of about 45 minutes each. New data must be collected outside of class between Sessions 2 and 3.

What to plan ahead of time

▼ Prepare a large piece of chart paper to record the initial data; you will need to

save these data and possibly add more later.

Alternatively, provide stick-on notes for making a large class graph directly on the chalkboard. You can make your own stick-on notes using a glue stick with a removable adhesive (such as Dennison's Tack-a-Note), which allows you to stick any piece of paper to the board and remove it for reuse without damage (Sessions 1 and 3).

▼ Find out the typical family size for your community by making a call to your city's or town's government offices. Census data are on record, and officials are usually glad to provide such information over the phone (Session 2).

▼ Duplicate Student Sheet 2 (page 90) for each student (Session 2).

Important mathematical ideas

Defining a question and establishing techniques for collecting data. Making decisions about how to count or measure is a key aspect of data analysis. Decisions about data collection have a profound effect on the eventual outcome of statistical work. Discussions about defining the question take a good deal of time at first. This time investment will pay off as your students become well-informed future consumers of statistics.

Making quick sketches of the data. Graphs need not always be tidy and perfect. Often a quick sketch of the data is more valuable than a final draft graph. Encourage your students to use simple line plots to display their data. Look back at the Teacher Note, *Line plot: A quick way to show the shape of the data* (page 23).

Understanding that sampling is one way to gather data about a population.
Sometimes census data are available for a particular population (as some data are for the whole nation). More often, however, complete data are not available. In those cases, sampling is often used to get data about the population in question.

Developing the notion of bias in samples.
The overall pattern of family size in your city or town may be quite different from that shown by your students' families. For one thing, there are single-person families that will not be represented in a sample of elementary school children. It is also possible that your class's family size is larger (or smaller) than what is typical for the population of your city or town. Perhaps, for instance, those with large families are more likely to attend one school, while those with smaller families attend another. Encourage your students to question samples on the basis of representativeness: Was the sample chosen in such a way that it is likely to give a good picture of the population? At the same time, students should understand that sampling is a powerful technique for obtaining information. Taking samples, although inexact, can provide a good approximation of a population. ■

SESSION 1 ACTIVITIES

Introducing the problem: How big is a family?

We are going to spend some time looking at family size in our city/town. We'll be sampling the population to get some good data. First, let's start our sample by looking at the families in this class. How many people are in your family? How can we investigate the question?

Some of your students may have done this activity in previous classes, as part of the *Used Numbers* unit, *Statistics: The Shape of the Data*. If they have, encourage them to share their methods and results, and ask them whether they believe the class results will be similar to those they collected previously.

☛ Be sure to wait until the next session to reveal the "official" town figures.

Defining the question: How do we count family members?

Let's start to collect the data from our class. How big are your families? Whom will you count?

This question will generate a great deal of discussion. There is no clear-cut definition of family that takes into account all of the family configurations in your classroom!

Every group that we have watched investigate this question has engaged in an extended discussion of whom to count. This is an important aspect of data analysis—initial decisions about defining what to count profoundly affect the outcomes of statistical studies.

Allow 15–20 minutes for students to think about, react to, and weigh a variety of definitions of family. Try to avoid voting as a means of settling disagreements. Discussing and redefining their ideas will bring students to consensus and enable them all to share ownership of the definition they agree on. In such a discussion, try to help students determine what aspects of family size they consider most important, and find ways to incorporate those into their definition. See the Dialogue Box, *How do I count my family?* (page 29).

Collecting and recording data: Counting who is in your family

When the definition of family has been decided and is clear to everyone, ask students how many are in their families, according to their own definition, and quickly record the information a line plot or a tally. See the Teacher Note, *Line plot: A quick way to show the shape of the data* (page 23). You may want to have students use stick-on notes to record their results on a large line plot on the board.

Summarizing data: What can we conclude about our family size?

Let's look at these data together. How would you describe the results? What can we say about the typical family size for our class?

As the class looks at the data display, allow time for careful reflection. Students may need some help in focusing on the typical family size. For more information, see the Teacher Note, *Summarizing data: What's typical?* (page 31).

There may well be more than one interpretation of these data. Students may have learned to find the median or the mode: "The middle family has 4 people in it, so I think that's typical"; or, "The number with the most kids is 5—there's more there, so I think

that's the most typical." On the other hand, some may choose to look at ranges to try to capture a larger part of the whole-class data: "There's the most of the kids at 3 and 4 and 5. So if we say around 3 or 4 or 5, we get almost everyone."

As long as the results are based on the data that were collected, and students agree that the interpretations seem valid to them, you can accept different results within the same class. For more information on handling discussions that may involve some conflict of ideas, see the Teacher Note: *Mathematical discussions: Challenging ideas* (page 32).

Today we've defined our question, collected and looked at data, and made some statements about your typical family size. Later we'll be comparing our data with that of a larger group—our whole city/town. ∎

How many in our families?

"DIALOGUE BOX
How do I count my family?

Students are usually eager to discuss their families. As this is a topic of intense personal interest and concern, allow adequate time for everyone to participate in the discussion. Diversity in family structure is to be expected and respected. Students may bring up many kinds of family situations. What about grandparents, aunts, or uncles who live with them? If we're going to count Eddie's grandmother who lives with him, what about Irena's grandfather who lives upstairs from her, or Rafael's aunt with whom he spends the summers? Students often talk about parts of their families living in different locations ("When I'm at my dad's house, there are three of us there, but when I'm at my mom's, there are four of us there"). Older siblings who no longer live at home, foster children, people temporarily living with the family, permanent members of the household who are not relatives, and even pets have been brought up in these discussions ("My sister only comes home to borrow the car, so can I count her as a quarter of a person?").

Teachers can handle these discussions sensitively so that all family styles and arrangements are acknowledged and accepted. But eventually students must come to some consensus about a definition of family. There is, of course, no single right

(Dialogue Box continued)

way to construct this definition; in fact, different groups have settled on different definitions, depending on how they wanted to pursue their investigation. These have included: "You and your parents and your sisters and brothers, regardless of where they live"; "Everyone who lives in your house right now"; or, as one group of adults finally decided, "Everyone who uses the same bathroom as you"!

The definition can be constructed to reflect what the students are most interested in. For example, if they want to know how many people actually share their living space, they would want to count everyone in the household; but if they are more interested in how many brothers and sisters people have, they might want to count all siblings, no matter where they live. Students may want to vote on a definition, but discourage this approach. As amateur statisticians, students shouldn't select a definition because it is the most popular, but because it will lead them to collect the data that will best give them the information they want.

As an example of such a discussion, these fifth and sixth graders were just beginning to define the membership in their families.

KELLEY: What do you do if your family is divorced? I'm considering my mom and dad together. So it's me and my sister and my mom and dad—4.

MARGOT: At my dad's there are 2 people and at my mother's there are 6. So it's 8.

TIM: 6-1/2.

What is the half?

TIM: A friend.

Not family?

TIM: OK, 6.

BEVERLY: Can I count the people who live in my house? They're very close. My mother went to college with two of them—I call their kids cousins. So I'll say 9.

GREG: I don't think you should count friends even if they're really close. Because they're not family.

MARIAN: My father lives in Ohio so that wouldn't be near enough.

ALICE: Are we counting family or only people you live with?

ETHLYN: In my house there's one family, 3 people.

BILLY: I have a brother, but he's adopted.

PETER: I think he should be counted.

Hold it! You've all got different ideas about whom to include and whom to exclude. Let's make an overall definition so that we have comparable data. That way everyone will answer the same question. So who do you want to include?

MANUEL: Everyone who lives with you.

PETER: Not everyone. Not if they pay rent.

KIMBERLEY: Yeah. If they pay rent they aren't family.

OK, so the first thing to do is to write that down.

[*Writes "don't pay rent."*]

BETTINA: What if they're like part-time family? My stepsister goes back and forth between her dad and my dad because her mom is my stepmother. So does she count like a real sister or like a fraction?

GREG: If they aren't there a lot, they shouldn't count. Like my sister is off at college and she isn't there mostly, except when she comes home on vacations and then she's there a lot.

Bettina thinks that her "part" sister should count; Greg thinks his "part" sister shouldn't. Can we make a decision about "part" families?

☞ During this very long discussion, the teacher teased out more and more elements of a definition of family membership. Eventually the class agreed that they had a working definition. They kept this definition:

Your family is everyone who lives in your house most of the time, except not if they pay rent and not if they spend more than half of their time somewhere else during regular weeks. But if they are off at college or grown up but they're still your sister or brother, you can count them. ∎

Summarizing data: What's typical?

Summarizing data is one of the main tasks of data analysis. A data set starts out as an unordered set of many values. In data analysis, we need to capture the essence of the shape of the data through a few key numbers so that we can describe and compare data sets without referring to all the values.

As consumers of statistics, our encounters with data sets are often through these key numbers: the average (mean) number of people in a U.S. household in 1985 was 2.69 (a record low); in the same year, the median age of the population was 31.5; also in 1985, more women in the U.S. work force were employed in "administrative support" than in any other category of occupations, while the mode for men was the category of "precision production, craft, and repair."*

Statisticians try to capture the essence of the data by identifying its center, or average, and then describing how the data are spread around that center. We are used to thinking of "average" as the arithmetic mean, the number obtained by adding all the values

and dividing by the number of values. Actually, there are many possible measures of average. The *mean* (used above as a measure of people per household) is one; *median* (used above for the age of the population) and *mode* (used above in the occupational statistics) are other measures of average.

In order for students to understand these summary methods, they need experience with situations in which they feel a need for summarizing the data. Deciding what is usual, typical, or central for a group is one reason to summarize data. Students will encounter the question "What's typical?" in many of their data analysis investigations. For comparing two sets of data, they will also find it necessary to summarize each data set. For example, in order to determine whether the number of people per household in the U.S. is increasing or decreasing, we must capture the shape of large data sets in a few numbers so that we can compare data from different years.

Students begin to understand how to summarize data by developing their own approaches during the investigations. For example, in an investigation comparing the heights of first graders and fourth graders, one fourth grader hit upon an important notion about how to summarize a data set: "We should find the number that's maybe in the middle or that all the other numbers are crowded around."

Chances are your students already know how to compute the arithmetic mean or, as they may call it, the "average." Although this type of average is often taught in elementary school, research has shown that the nature and significance of the mean is often not understood, even by older students and adults.

We recommend that upper elementary teachers discourage any use of the mean until students have had extended exposure to data analysis. Students need experience with a great variety of data sets before they are ready to understand how the arithmetic mean relates to the data it represents. Another unit in the *Used Numbers* series, *Statistics: Middles, Means, and In-Betweens,* provides appropriate experiences for learning about the mean.

In the meantime, discourage your students from applying the add-'em-all-up-and-divide-by-the-number approach they may have learned with little understanding. If a student says, "We could find the average," you can respond something like this: "Yes, we could. Actually, there are many kinds of averages that you'll learn about as you go on in mathematics. Averages are often ways of saying what's typical about a set of data. Right now we're going to be inventing our own ways of deciding what's typical, and later in this unit you're going to learn about one kind of average." ■

---

*U.S. Bureau of the Census, Current Population Reports, Special Studies Series P-23, No. 150, *Population Profile of the United States: 1984/85,* (Washington, DC: U.S. Government Printing Office, 1987).

✏ TEACHER NOTE
Mathematical discussions: Challenging ideas

One of the most important ideas in mathematics is that one's assertions should be subject to scrutiny and challenge. The history of mathematics is the history of debate and discussion, yet we do not see much discussion in most mathematics classes.

In fact, many students are convinced that there is always one right answer and one "best" procedure in mathematics class. This idea often leads them to be nervous if their answers or strategies seem to conflict. But discussion about different strategies, different approaches, and different solutions lies at the heart of mathematics. Encouraging students to make assertions, to base their arguments on data, to state their reasons, and to ask others clarifying questions is a vital aspect of teaching mathematics.

Challenging students' ideas is a delicate matter, yet it can be a very effective way of probing to find out what your students are thinking and to help them clarify and extend their own ideas. Many teachers find that the best way of examining students' ideas is to ask questions that invite them to explain their reasons:

Say more about that.

Can you give me an example?

How do the data tell you that?

Another technique is to ask students to relate their ideas to other students' ideas:

Is this like Emilio's idea?

Are your reasons the same as Isaac's?

Yolanda's theory and Benjamin's are very different. Could they both work? Can you think of any evidence that would help us know if either of these theories work?

A third way teachers sometimes probe students' ideas is to give counter examples or suggest other experiments:

Some other fifth [sixth] graders say that samples are never right. What would you tell them?

Do you think anything would change if we collected more data from different fifth graders?

Do you think if we did the same survey again today, the results would be the same as the one we did yesterday?

You may have other techniques that work for you. Once ideas are flowing, you may find that the students themselves make many suggestions, ask each other probing questions, and help to formulate ideas. Until then, however, it is important to keep discussion alive. Researchers have found that simply waiting 3 seconds after asking a question gives students time to organize their thinking and to develop some of their ideas before answering. Three seconds seems like a very long time when you're used to much faster answers, but students need to feel that they have time to think. Hurrying them to an answer defeats the whole purpose of mathematical discussions. ■

SESSION 2 ACTIVITIES

Comparing a sample with a census: What's typical of the city or town?

I telephoned City Hall and found out the average size of a family in [name of your city or town]. They told me that the typical family size is [number]. How does this compare with the results for our class?

Ask students to react to the two sets of results, their figures for average family size in their class, and the figure for the larger population, suggesting reasons for the similarities or differences. Encourage them to think about the population that the "official" figure represents.

Your students may have some interesting analyses of these data. In one classroom, a student insisted that any figures which came from the census were wrong because they were hopelessly outdated: "It's real old numbers. Even before we were born or before we moved here. So the numbers should be higher now because there's more of us here." In another class, students felt that a new apartment complex had decreased the overall family size in their community: "Mostly there are single people over in the apartments, so that makes families get smaller and smaller."

When your students have talked and thought about the comparison and contrast of these results, ask them to turn their attention to the issue of sampling.

Evaluating the sample: Are we a good sample of the town?

We've collected and analyzed family-size data for ourselves. Now I'd like you to consider whether we are a representative sample of all the families who live here. Do you think our class data fairly represent all of the families in the town? On the basis of our family size, could we make valid claims about the family size for the whole community?

Ask students to think of ways in which their families are and are not representative of all the families in their community. You will find that your students will have some good informal ways of evaluating their representativeness as a sample. Allow plenty of time for them to share their ideas.

Improving the sample: Going beyond the class

What could we do to select a more adequate sample of family size in our city/town? Today you will work in small groups to outline plans for getting a better sample. Take 15 minutes now to talk together about what you think we can do to get better data. I'll ask you to share your ideas with everyone. We'll actually be using some of your plans to collect data, so try to keep them simple.

Cluster students in groups of three or four. Focus their attention on what's missing from their sample of families, and how they could improve the sample to better represent the

population of their city/town. A recorder will be needed in each small group to keep track of ideas as they arise.

As the small groups talk, circulate among them. Help students clarify their thinking about getting data from a more representative sample. Ask them questions about their reasons ("Why do you want to collect data from the people in the apartment building?"); ask about the logical consequences of their ideas ("So how many people will we have to ask?"); ask about how the group is reaching agreement ("Does everyone go along with that plan, or do you have other ideas to contribute?").

When the groups have outlined some strategies for collecting more information, call them back together to develop an overall plan for the class.

Designing a new sampling effort: Collecting more data

You've all come up with some good ideas about how to improve our sample of the families in our city/town. Let's compare ideas now and see what's the best way we can collect more data to use in class.

Ask students to share their ideas. List them on a board or chart that everyone can see. Help the class analyze the suggested plans and reach some consensus about how to get a more representative sample of families.

Consider the practicality of what students can actually do to collect data for the next class. If the "best" plan is too ambitious, can they do *part* of it? Remember that the goal is to collect some data from a more representative sample of families in the town, to see whether it affects the results that students got by using only their class as a sample.

Planning data collection: What question will we ask?

How many people will each of you ask? How will you write down the information?

Help the class decide who will ask whom what and how. Students need to review the definition of "family" they established in Session 1. Are they likely to run into any problems with this definition? Are they satisfied with their definition? Will it apply to all the new cases they might run into?

Take some time for role playing so that the students are sure about their task. Have volunteers simulate the survey situation to practice explaining the project and their definition of family, and asking for people's family size. They can use Student Sheet 2, *Getting more family data*, to record information. On this form, there is a place to identify each family in the sample. Here students might write the family's name, address, apartment number—anything that would allow them to doublecheck their data later.

It is very important that students leave with a strong sense of whom they will ask, what they will ask, what they can say to those from whom they collect information, and how to record the data they collect. ■

SESSION 3 ACTIVITIES

Adding to the class family data: Do new data change our results?

Let's record and analyze the new data you have collected on family size in our city/town. Will someone remind us why we decided to collect more data on family size? What question are we investigating?

Let students spend some time talking about how they collected their new data. Were there any hard parts? Any surprises? Did they find cases that their definition didn't cover?

Ask the students to record their raw data on the board where everyone can see them. When the new data are complete, ask whether the students want to add them to the class data or keep them separate for comparison. That is, should these be treated as separate samples, or does the class want to look at all the data together as one sample? This point is worth discussing at some length; ask students to make a case for whichever way they decide to treat the sample data.

Looking again at the family data: Adding the new information

Spend some time analyzing the family-size data.

What do you see? What do these additional data tell you? Has the range of family size changed? Are there any new family sizes represented? Has the shape of the data changed?

From this larger sample, what would you say now about the city/town's family size?

Ask students to explain their reasoning as they make their claims.

Considering the representativeness of the sample

Ask the students what predictions they would now make about family size in the city/town from their sample data.

Do you think your new data have improved the quality of the sample? Does its increased size make a difference in the results? How much confidence do you have in this new "typical" family-size figure?

If students feel that this sample is still not representative (perhaps it does not include any one-person families, or any two-person families), ask them how that would affect their predictions about the town's family size. Encourage them to talk about their results in a way that reflects the sample's adequacy. For example: "We found that the typical family size was 4 in our sample, but we didn't have anyone who lives alone, so we think in the whole town it's a little lower than 4."

Reporting on sample adequacy is important in statistics. Sometimes inadequacies in sampling are unavoidable; the important thing is to report the characteristics of the sample so that inadequacies can be taken into account.

Support a free-ranging discussion of this new sample. Would students want to go further in finding a sample they believe to be representative?

Summary: When should we count everyone?

If the government of a city wants to find out about, for instance, the typical family size, or the average age of its citizens, or the number of homeless, is it right for them to choose a sample and to generalize from that sample? What would be the advantage of doing that? When would it be less appropriate?

It's important to remember that samples are reasonable shortcuts when counting everyone is not possible or too difficult. It's also important to remember that finding a representative sample may be difficult, and that for some information, it's not reasonable to take any shortcuts. That's why the government takes a census every ten years; they need to be sure that they have all the information they may need until new information comes in.

Extensions

▼ If there is a political issue in your town, you might want to have your students design a sampling plan for the school board or the city government to use when collecting opinion data.

▼ As an example of a real-life data collection problem, you might want to encourage your class to think about how the government should count the homeless. Would a sample be appropriate?

▼ If you have the videotapes for *The Voyage of the Mimi*, published by Sunburst, you might want to show Episodes 2, 3, and 4 and Expedition 2, in which the scientists on the voyage train the younger students in taking samples of whale behaviors. This is an excellent real-life example of how to take samples of a population that can't be seen.

▼ Students might enjoy a study of the census. At this writing, the national 1990 census is underway, and there will be a lot of public information available. Students may be aware of census materials coming to their homes. Educational materials about the census are available from: U.S. Census Bureau, 2601 North Howard Street, Baltimore, MD 21218, Attention: Lorraine Taylor.

You may want to invite a working statistician who deals with demographics in your community to come talk with the class about what he or she does and what the population trends in your area seem to be. ■

IN THE CHIPS

INVESTIGATION OVERVIEW

What happens

Students sample a large collection of different-colored plastic chips and predict color distribution of the population using information from their sample. After making a prediction from one sample, they take another sample of the same size and make another prediction from these new data. Results from these two predictions are compared with samples of a very different size taken later the investigation.

The activities take one class session of about 45 minutes.

What to plan ahead of time

▼ Provide 400 plastic chips (300 red, 100 white) in a transparent container. You can use plastic chips designed for card games, which are available in variety stores, or counting chips, which can be purchased from suppliers of educational materials. Alternatively, set up a collection of any object that comes in two colors, such as buttons or marbles, or even dried beans or pasta in two colors or two distinct shapes.

Important mathematical ideas

Taking different samples of a large population. Students develop their own methods of inferring information about the population from a sample. They compare methods and talk with each other about their predictions.

Understanding that the *size of the sample* is important in predicting characteristics about a population. Students already have informal ideas about which gives better information, small or large samples—often expressed as a preference for taking a complete census whenever possible. Upper elementary students are concerned with having "enough information" to describe or make predictions about the population, so they want to find a "good" sample size.

Recognizing the validity of sampling. While using information taken from samples may sometimes be inexact, in many instances such information permits us to make reasonable predictions about the population. ■

SESSION ACTIVITIES

Considering the problem: Choosing the size of a sample

We've been talking about sampling and about being able to make predictions about a population from our samples. How well does this work? Sometimes pretty well, sometimes not so well. One of the factors you decided was important was the size of the sample.

Hold up the container of chips, and explain the sampling task for today's investigation.

I have a population of 400 chips here. There are two colors. Your task, as a whole group, is to make a good estimate of the number of each color by sampling the population. You'll figure out what size sample to take and how to take it. What size sample do you want to try?

Write students' ideas about appropriate sample size on the board. It's important to let all the ideas surface, and to encourage students to talk with each other about their ideas. For an example of what may happen, see the Dialogue Box, *Choosing the size of a sample* (page 41).

Choosing sample size is an important discussion topic. Be sure that you stay neutral and allow the class to make its own decision. Ask students for reasons for their choices. Why does Jeremy want to predict based on a sample of 20? Why does Elena insist that they need a sample much closer to 100?

Be prepared for a student to suggest that they count them all. An appropriate response to that suggestion is, "Yes, if we counted them all we'd be sure. But we need to figure out what to do when groups are so large we *can't* count them all—like everyone in New England, or every driver in the United States."

Now that you've decided how many chips you want to take in your sample, you need to decide how to take the sample. Did you have a method in mind?

You may want to add your suggestions to those of your students as they generate possible methods for sampling these chips. Some classes have decided to have individual students each select some part of the sample and then add them all up; some have asked a small group to do it for the whole class.

Students sometimes misunderstand and treat the selection of chips as a competition ("I got more reds!" "Blue is gonna win, I know!"). If that happens, you may want to say something about sample selection not being competitive.

It is important that the sample selection be as random as possible. Students might suggest shaking up the chips before selection, or not looking at the chips while selecting a small sample. We have found that selection and counting by individual students is the most time-consuming method, but also the one that engages students the most.

Recording and analyzing the data: Chips in the sample and chips in the population

After the sample of chips is sorted, counted, and totaled, write the total for each of the two colors on the chalkboard. It is also a good idea to show a sketchy bar graph next to those numbers, because some students will want to use visual cues in addition to numbers as they make their predictions about the color distribution in population of chips.

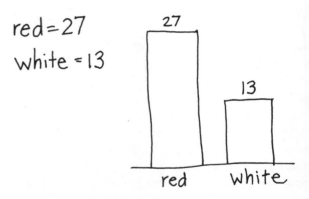

Spend some time looking at the profile of the sample. See the Teacher Note, *Looking at the profile of a sample* (page 42).

What can we tell from these results? How would you describe these results? What are your predictions about how many of each color are in the population of chips?

As students make the transition from looking at relative proportion of colors in the sample to determining the relative proportion of colors in the population, it is important to talk with them about their methods and their approaches. Not all your students will feel comfortable with the fact that a sample cannot guarantee that they are right. Help them see that their careful selection of a method, and their use of that method to infer the distribution of colors in the population, are part of assuring that their sample is as representative as possible.

Everyone has different methods for making predictions about populations from the information in samples. Describe your way of doing it, so we can all think about it together.

☞ Keep the "real" number of each color secret at this point. They students are going to try another sample size first. Otherwise, they may think that the object of this exercise is to be correct rather than to explore the possibilities of trying different methods of sampling.

Reconsidering the problem: Choosing another sample

Return the first sample of chips to the container and shake them up thoroughly before you let the students select another sample.

What do you think will happen if you take another sample of the same size? Will you get the same numbers of reds and whites, or will they be different?

Students often believe that another sample will be exactly the same. It's hard to understand that samples can vary and still accept the idea that they can provide useful information. For more information, see the Teacher Note, *Samples vary!* (page 43).

From your first sample, you think there are [number] red chips and [number] white ones in the population of 400. Let's try another sample, to see whether you get a similar result or if you want to change your predictions.

Students use the same methods as before to select a sample, tabulate the results, and predict color distribution in the population. Do they get some different results? Do they want to change their predictions? Be prepared for some serious discussion if there are real differences—your class may want to take three or four more samples as they try to get more comfortable with making predictions.

Looking at a different sample size: Are the results similar?

After students have taken at least two samples of the same size, suggest that they try a new sample size—perhaps one that is a good deal smaller or a good deal larger than their original sample.

Students again select the sample and sort and count the chips by color. Write the numbers on the board and make a sketchy bar graph, as before. What predictions will students make from this sample? Allow some time for students to talk about their methods of extrapolating from the sample to the population.

Analyzing differences: Comparing the results of these samples

From the first sample, you thought that there would be [number] red chips and [number] white chips in the population. From the second, you predicted [number] red chips and [number] white chips. From this one, you have said you think there are [number] red and [number] white. How can you explain those results? If you had to go with one prediction, which would you choose? Why?

Reveal the actual proportions of colors in the chip collection, showing on the board the actual profile of the population and the profile of each sample. See the Teacher Note, *Looking at the profile of a sample* (page 42).

Spend some time eliciting student ideas about why the samples may be misleading or why they are representative. Ask students to compare how representative the different samples were. Explain that when statisticians are doing sampling, they have some mathematical rules that help them select the "best" sample size. We won't be going into the rules in this series; it's enough for students to know that the sample size may affect both the results and the confidence they can have in those results.

Extension: Sampling another population

Many teachers have used the Mars Company's M&M candy packages to explore samples of a population with more than two attributes—in this case, six colors. Each small bag of M&M candies represents a sample of the population of M&Ms; there is enough variability in results to make them good material for exploration.

Your students will find that although there is a good deal of difference from sample to sample (one student was very disturbed to find a bag with only one red M&M), these differences tend to wash out as they collect data from more and more samples.

The Mars Company has provided the following information about the proportions of the six colors of M&Ms that they produce:

Red	20%
Brown	30%
Tan	20%
Yellow	10%
Green	10%
Orange	10%

💬 DIALOGUE BOX
Choosing the size of a sample

In this combination fifth-sixth grade classroom, the teacher has put together a collection of three colors of marbles for her students to sample. There are 200 each of blue and red, and 100 yellow marbles. The students are deciding on how many marbles to include in their sample. They know that the population of marbles is 500, and that it includes only those three colors.

Your job is to find out how many of each color there are in the population. How many marbles would you need for a sample?

ISAAC: You didn't tell us whether they're equal!

I won't! Your job is to figure that out by sampling the population of marbles.

Yolanda: Five.

Why?

YOLANDA: You can multiply 5 times 100 to get 500, so we just make it 100 times bigger and then you can tell.

GREG: That's too small. Take all 500!

OK, then we'd know _for sure_, but it's against the rules right now.

KIMBERLEY: Fifty, because 50's a multiple of 500. You could multiply the results by 10.

SHARON: I say 250, because it's exactly half.

ALICE: Yes! That's _exactly_ what I was going to say. You could just double it.

BENJAMIN: What if there's only one yellow?

Didn't we find out before that there would be room for some errors? We'll get as close as we can!

MARY LOU: Me and Bettina both agree it should be 25.

Why?

MARY LOU: Because it's a good number.

SHARON: We could take 10 each, we would all have a few.

PETER: Let's try 5 each, because 20 kids times 5 marbles is 100. It's about 1/5 of the total.

BRIDGET: Yeah, that way we could each get the same amount and we don't have to do hard math when we figure out about all the marbles.

MANUEL: I want to try Peter's way. It sounds good.

Do many people agree? How many would like to use this method?

[Most of the students raise their hands.]

MARY LOU: But maybe we need something three goes into because there are three colors.

What do others think?

YOLANDA: I don't think so. We need to find out how many in 500. So 3 can't go into that

evenly anyhow.

GREG: And what's one marble when we're looking at 500?

What do you mean, Greg?

GREG: Well, it's silly to worry too much about the details because we don't get an exact number anyhow. It's really _around_ a number and not exact because we can't tell unless we count them all.

Are you ready to decide how to pick out the sample now?

☞ In this discussion, students have consistently shown a good grasp of the fact that the sample will be used to decide the proportion of each color of marbles in the population. They are aware of the need to select a "sensible" sample. The teacher lets them discuss the question broadly, and they are able to reach a consensus. ∎

TEACHER NOTE
Looking at the profile of a sample

WILLIAM: We got 43 in the sample that are red, but we need to find out what it would be if it were 6 times bigger, because our sample is a sixth of the population. So we multiply . . . um, um . . . 43 times 6 and . . . um . . . then we get 258.

And what does that tell you?

WILLIAM: It's 258.

What's 258?

WILLIAM: I forgot.

William has forgotten why he multiplied 43 times 6 in the first place. Often the effort of finding a precise total defeats a student's ability to reason through a problem. We need to help students estimate, do mental calculation, and have some ways of finding totals without losing the original question.

Because your students may not be facile at manipulating large numbers, it is important to present information visually whenever samples are taken. Thus, with a plastic chip sample of 80, you may get 58 red chips and 22 white ones. Graphing the data as shown below may better enable students to see the proportion of each color in the total than using only the numbers would.

Discussing the sample can help students make some decisions about what the sample might show about the population. You can help them think about the shape of the sample data and decide, if the shape is approximately the same in the population, how that will look.

It may help your students to think of ways of enlarging the picture that the sample provides, keeping the key features in proportion. If you have an overhead projector, you can demonstrate how that would work by taking the sample data and projecting them as a larger but similarly proportioned image. Calculators, too, can be used as a matter of course to do calculations. However, it is not necessary that students be precise when they make inferences from a sample. If they multiply 43 times 6 and decide that will be a little more than 240, that's certainly close enough.

Your job is to help them attend to the relative proportions of characteristics in the sample, and to maintain a picture of the sample

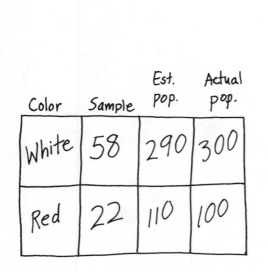

Color	Sample	Est. Pop.	Actual Pop.
White	58	290	300
Red	22	110	100

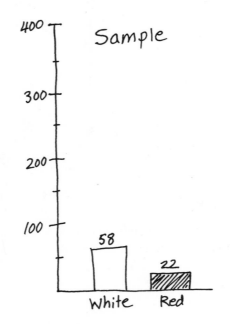

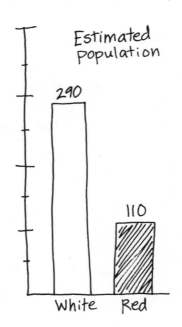

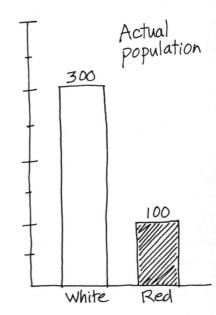

when they start to thinking about the population. The details will be less important than the overall picture.

It is very tempting to use this lesson to emphasize the mathematics of percent or ratio. However, most students at this age are still very experientially-based thinkers. Although some seem to be able to do ratio and percentage problems, most of them have not really mastered the abstractions involved. They are likely to be confused if the emphasis shifts from "what do you think makes sense?" to "let's look at a routine for finding the correct answer." Remember, sampling provides estimates of the population—it is approximate. The important idea is for the class to generate *many* ways of predicting and see that each student can confidently make a prediction based on some logic. Reasons are more important than computational accuracy. ■

✎ TEACHER NOTE
Samples vary!

One class took a sample of a population of 500 red, blue, and yellow marbles. In the first sample of 100, they had 41 blue, 19 yellow, and 40 red. Because there were nearly twice as many of the blues and reds as of the yellows, they decided that there would be 200 blues, 100 yellows, and 200 reds in the population.

Confident, the students replaced these marbles, re-mixed them, and took another sample of 100. This time there were 32 blue, 21 yellow, and 47 red. Based on multiplying each number by 5 (because there were five times more marbles in the population than in the sample), they now thought there would be 160 blues, 105 yellows, and 235 reds.

This completely threw the class, because the blues and reds no longer seemed close to being equal. There were about 50 percent more reds than blues. One child suggested that they should average out the results between the two samples. Another suggested that they take three more samples and then decide. A third wanted to count the population to decide which sample was right.

The teacher, who knew that the first sample yielded the "correct" information, was puzzled as to how to proceed. She remembered that samples could vary and could

yield a variety of results, so she waited for the students to talk about their reactions and then encouraged them to take three more samples. These were very similar to the students' first sample, and on the basis of that, the students were content to keep to their original prediction.

The students welcomed the information that there was variability in samples, and they understood that sometimes the results were "out there," as one child termed it. They were reassured when their teacher told them that opinion polls always included statements about the margin of error—precisely because one sample, although still a good sample, might yield predictions that were a little "out there." ■

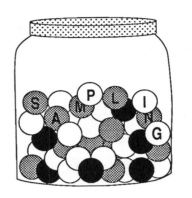

Statistics:
Prediction and
Sampling

PART 2
Using sampling

CATS: SAMPLING A POPULATION OF ANIMALS

GETTING TO KNOW OURSELVES
Green eyes XXX
Blue eyes XX
Yellow eyes XXXXX
Likes to eat fish
XXXXXXXXXX
Licks paws clean
XXXXX

INVESTIGATION OVERVIEW

What happens

Students work with a sample of data about 24 real cats to determine whether they can decide from this sample what is typical of cats. They organize, display, and summarize given data, then collect data about additional cats themselves in order to expand the sample. Students analyze the new data to decide whether to change their descriptions of a typical cat.

The activities take four class sessions of about 45 minutes each. New data must be collected outside of class between Sessions 1 and 3.

The Session 2, 3 and 4 activities can be done using only the printed data, but are much more effective on the computer. The information provided can be entered into whatever data base you have available.

What to plan ahead of time

▼ Provide a set of the 24 cat cards at the end of this book, ideally one set for each small group; see page 97 for more information (Sessions 1, 2, 3).

▼ Provide materials for making sketch graphs (Sessions 1 and 3) and presentation graphs (Session 3).

▼ Duplicate Student Sheet 3 (page 91) for each student (homework following Session 1). Duplicate Student Sheet 4 (page 92) for each student, or make a single copy to keep at each computer (Session 2).

▼ Provide measuring equipment for student use at home after Session 1. Cloth measuring tapes are best because they are flexible.

▼ Become familiar with a computer data base, such as *Bank Street Filer* or *AppleWorks* for the Apple II computer. Set up the fields for the cat data, and enter the data about the 24 cats into your program. This will take some preparation time— allow at least an hour. Plan a strategy for helping your students use the computer to explore data bases. See the Teacher Note, *About data bases* (page 53). Schedule time for small groups (pairs seem to work well) so that they can explore the computer and learn to use the data base of cat information. (Optional, Session 2).

Important mathematical ideas

Collecting and recording data that involve more than one variable. Until now, students have looked at one variable in a sample and have confined their analysis to that variable. Now the sample data include many characteristics.

Analyzing sample data that are both categorical and numerical to describe a population. The given data about cats are both categorical (color of fur, color of eyes) and numerical (weight, length of tail). Encourage your students to look for landmarks in these data; you may need to remind them that the categorical data do not have a median or mean, because they do not have an intrinsic order. There can, however, be a mode for categorical data—the value that appears most frequently in the data set.

Using a given sample to make claims about a very large population. In earlier investigations, students have used themselves as a sample or have selected their own samples of populations. They are now being asked to think about a population that is very large, and to select samples and decide how well these samples approximate the population of cats.

Using technology to facilitate data retrieval and organization. Students can easily manipulate the cat card set to get the information they want. However, as the data set grows bigger, it is more difficult to do this by hand. Using computer technology allows students to experience its power in collecting, organizing, and retrieving data. ■

SESSION 1 ACTIVITIES

Becoming familiar with the sample

Listen to this scientific description of a familiar animal:

> *Felis catus. . . .* **There are more than 30 different breeds of domestic cat, and the average measurements of several popular breeds are: head and body length, 460 mm [18.11 inches], and tail length, 300 mm [11.81 inches].***

What animal is described here? When a biologist describes an animal this way, where do you think the data come from?

The domestic cat has not been systematically studied, although data have been collected and analyzed in some locations. A sample of cats allows students to compare their results with those cited above.

Today you will begin working with a sample of a population that is so large, we can't possibly count and check it. I am going to give you a card set of information about that sample.

Assign students to small groups and hand out the cat cards, one packet for each group. After students have had time to browse informally through the cat cards, allow time for them to make observations or ask questions about the data set. You will

---

*R.M. Nowak and J.L. Paradiso, *Walker's Mammals of the World*, Vol. 2, 4th ed. (Baltimore: The Johns Hopkins University Press, 1983), page 1068.

probably get some stories about other cats—tell students that they will have a chance later to add data about cats they know personally.

You are going to decide what's typical about cats in this sample. On the cards, you'll find data (including names) for each cat, and you may be able to find out some other things about the cats—such as distinctive markings—from the pictures. Each group is going to be responsible for doing research on one characteristic of cats. Look through the cards and decide what characteristic your group wants to investigate.

As the groups decide which of the characteristics they want to explore, write those on the chalkboard so that the whole class can see what is covered. Make sure that there's a reasonable balance between numerical and categorical data, and that groups choose different characteristics so the class can get an overall picture. When each group has chosen an attribute, ask them to spend 15–20 minutes collecting data from this sample, recording it, and deciding what's typical of this sample of cats.

When your group reports back to us in about 15 minutes to tell us what's typical of this sample of cats, you'll need to have data to support your claims. A sketch graph or line plot may help you present your findings.

As the groups work, circulate among them. This is an excellent time to observe your students' use of data analysis skills. See the

Teacher Note, *Taking information from the cats data base* (page 50).

Preliminary findings: What's typical of the sample?

Small groups report to the whole class about their findings. Keep track of them on the chalkboard or a large sheet of chart paper. Encourage the class to ask questions of each other as the findings are interpreted. You will end up with a list that might include statements such as these:

A typical cat:

> Has green or yellow eyes.
> Weighs around 8.5 pounds.
> Is 19 inches long.

Evaluating the sample: Are these cats representative?

Can we say that the characteristics you listed are typical of all cats? How well does this sample approximate the characteristics of the population? Are there any colors or kinds of cats missing?

Encourage your students to think about other cats they know or have seen. Are there any values that do not appear in these data? Students may notice that there are no cats with blue eyes in this set; likewise, there are no white cats. The set is definitely biased in the direction of older cats as well. Any of these facts, taken by itself, is not a sure sign

that the sample is not representative, but it can call into question the how well the sample represents the population.

Encourage students to talk about ways in which the set seems representative and ways in which it doesn't. Support their challenging each other and talking about their reasons for their claims. See the Teacher Note, *About this sample of cats* (page 51), for further information on the cat data. By now your students know that a sample needs to be big enough to represent the range of values in the population; this sample really isn't.

Homework: Gathering more data

To try to improve this sample by making it larger, you will collect some more data for homework. Each of you will be responsible for collecting data about one more cat.

Allow time for students to talk about where they will collect these data.

If you don't have a cat, ask whether you can collect data from a neighbor's cat or a friend's cat, or you may want to go to the animal shelter and collect data there. Remember, though, that you have to be careful! Please don't just walk up to a strange cat and try to measure it. Ask permission from the owner and make sure you have someone to help you.

Hand out copies of Student Sheet 3, *Collecting cat data.* Assign a due date for this measurement work, and ask students to describe how they will approach the task.

Role-playing the act of measuring a cat may help your students focus on some of the subtleties of the task. See the Teacher Note, *Measuring a cat* (page 52) for further information.

When your students write their cat data on Student Sheet 3, they will find a category called "other." They may want to include here some short, interesting comments about the cat that they decide to use as a member of the sample.

Extensions

▼ Describing an animal so precisely that you can easily differentiate it from others is very difficult! In some classes students have enjoyed the exercise of trying to describe a cat to a Martian. How could you describe it so that it isn't confused with, for instance, a skunk or a raccoon or a rabbit or a squirrel? Your students may enjoy a writing assignment based on this idea. What data need to be included? Can you consider a literary description to be data?

▼ Biological definitions also need to differentiate species of animals from similar species. Some of your students may want to read about the near neighbors of domestic cats and begin to explore how scientists classify genera and species of animals. *Walker's Mammals of the World*, quoted at the beginning of this investigation, is an excellent source of facts and observations about mammals. Your school or local librarian can help you find other good sources for your students.

▼ Describing animals is not always done "scientifically." Some cat or dog show judges have interesting ways of describing the animals they work with; for example, the ears of cocker spaniels are called "leather." Check to see if a local breeder or judge would be willing to come talk with your students about some additional animal attributes. To find out more about special cat characteristics, contact the Cat Fanciers' Association (CFA) or The International Cat Association (TICA) in your area, or a breeder or veterinarian listed in your yellow pages. ■

✏️ TEACHER NOTE
Taking information from the cats data base

Students work with the cat cards and later the computer data base to sort and organize information in order to come up with a description of a typical cat. What could students reasonably conclude from these data in describing a cat?

Color. The most important idea about color is that there is *wide variation*, both in color and in pattern. However, there are some limits to this variation. Questions raised here might include: What appear to be the most common colors of cats? How many fur colors are there? Are many cats striped?

Age. As one student pointed out, "Even though there's no one-month-old cat here, we know they all *were* one month old once." We can tell from this sample that cats can live to be 18 years old. Discussion questions: How long does a typical cat live? Is 18 a typical age for a cat? How old are they if we translate to human years? (The old rule of thumb is 1 cat year = 7 human years.)

Weight. These data are very spread out. They range from 6.5 pounds to 18 pounds, with a large clump of cats from 9 to 12 pounds. Half the cats are in this clump, and if we add the 8 and 8.5 pound cats, we account for nearly two-thirds of the cats

between 8 and 12 pounds. As more cats are added to the data, keep an eye on weight to see whether it changes. Are the younger cats lighter than the older cats?

Body length. The cats' body lengths range from 14 to 24 inches, with a median of 18.5 inches. There are two strong modes, one at 17 inches and one at 21 inches. Three-fourths of the cats fall between these two modes, from 17 to 21 inches. So the median seems to be a good indicator of where the data are centered. Questions: Are the shortest cats just younger? Are the longest cats also the heaviest cats? As more data come in, does it still appear to be true that cats generally range from about 17 to 21 inches? Are the two longest and the two shortest really unusual in the cat population?

Tail length. These data are very compact. More than half of the cats have either 11- or 12-inch tails. Adding the 13-inch tails accounts for two-thirds of the data. The median tail length is 11 inches. It could be argued that the typical cat has an 11- or 12-inch tail, and that the range is from 8.5 to 13 inches. Although the typical cat's tail may be in the 11- or 12-inch range, some cats do have very short tails. Questions: Is tail length related to body length? As data come in from your class, does the typical tail length change, or does this clump hold true?

Eye color. Cats seem, from these data, to have green or yellow eyes, with very little difference between the amount of data at each of the two values. Questions: Can cats have any other eye color? Do certain eye colors go with certain fur or pad colors? As data are added, do the yellow and green eyes continue to be represented evenly in the larger sample?

Paw pad color. Paw pad color data have two modes. Most cats have either pink or black pads. However, from this sample we can see other colors, and we can also see that cats' pads may have mixed colors. Questions: Is pad color related to fur color? Are any new colors added as your data come in?

Other. It's important to remind your students that other information about cats is helpful and interesting; for example, in the cat cards provided, it is interesting that Wally is Peeble's brother. Have your students included such miscellaneous information about their cats? Although they can't analyze the "other" information statistically, it adds a lot to their data base. Encourage them to add comments as they enter their own data. ■

✎TEACHER NOTE
About this sample of cats

This sample of cats is a classic example of a convenience sample. When the idea of taking a sample of cats was proposed, members of the *Used Numbers* team happily volunteered their own and their friends' cats as sources of data, including Rebecca Corwin's cats, Lady Jane Grey, Strawberry, and Gus, and Susan Jo Russell's cat, Alexander. Many of the cats belong to TERC staff members and friends.

To add to the data base conveniently, two staff members attended a cat show in Boston and took pictures of some of the entrants. Those included cats entered as household

pets and cats who were shelter animals waiting for adoption.

In this investigation, your class collects information about cats that they know. Thus, theirs is a convenience sample, too. When it is added to ours, the combined sample is a little more representative. You might ask your students how to improve the representativeness of the sample even further. Do they have suggestions?

The *Used Numbers* team would like a copy of your data so that we can keep collecting statistics about real cats. Please send it to:

Used Numbers Cat Data, c/o Corwin
TERC
2067 Massachusetts Avenue
Cambridge, MA 02140 ■

Lady

Gender:	female
Age:	10 years
Weight:	8.5 pounds
Body length:	17 inches
Tail length:	13 inches
Fur color:	gray, brown, and white stripes
Eye color:	yellow
Pad color:	black
Other:	

Statistics: Prediction and Sampling   © Dale Seymour Publications

Charcoal

Gender:	male
Age:	11 years
Weight:	12 pounds
Body length:	21 inches
Tail length:	13 inches
Fur color:	black and white
Eye color:	yellow
Pad color:	black
Other:	Charcoal has big feet.

Statistics: Prediction and Sampling   © Dale Seymour Publications

K.C.

Gender:	male
Age:	5 years
Weight:	16 pounds
Body length:	24 inches
Tail length:	12 inches
Fur color:	brown and black stripes, some white
Eye color:	yellow
Pad color:	black
Other:	

Statistics: Prediction and Sampling   © Dale Seymour Publications

✏️TEACHER NOTE
Measuring a cat

"I couldn't weigh my cat because she wouldn't stand on the scale."

"How come Kim got 34 inches for her cat's length, and my cat and all the others we saw only got around 19 or 20 inches?"

Measurement problems are very common in any branch of statistics. It's a good idea to talk with your students about the measurements they will be collecting, so that they can agree on a starting point and an ending point for various parts, such as the tail. Such a discussion is most effective when students can think about the problem and make their own decisions about the "marking-off places" on the cats.

Discuss techniques of cat measurement with your students. They will profit from thinking in advance about the necessary equipment and the help they will need in stretching out parts of cats (the tail) and in trying to get a cat to hold still. As we measured our own cat sample, we became quite skilled at rolling rulers or tape measures from cats' noses to their tail bases.

One teacher brought her daughter's stuffed toy cat into the classroom and had students demonstrate how they would get the measurements from the real cat they were going to use as a data source. Some of them used measuring tapes and some tried with rulers and yardsticks. The students had a good laugh, and they were able to wrestle in advance with the technical problems they were about to face.

Weighing a cat is a difficult matter when you don't know how. Students can ask owners, who may know how much the cat weighs from its veterinary records. Some students will suggest that they can stand on the scale, weigh themselves with and without the cat, and subtract the difference. In a home where a baby scale is available, students can weigh the cat directly—if the cat is willing.

Encourage students to enlist a helper for the measuring process. Some cats are so wiggly that it's hard to get any kind of measure without someone else holding them still.

Measurement methods, agreement on the landmarks of the object being measured, and efforts at standardizing measurement are important parts of all statistics research. These processes allow mathematicians to collect data that are consistent. ∎

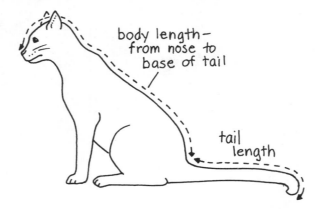

body length—from nose to base of tail

tail length

SESSION 2 ACTIVITIES

Browsing in a data base: A technological interlude

☛ This session is best done on computers. If you do not have a computer or a data base program that your students can use, your students can still browse in the data base using the cards provided.

Organizing and manipulating data is one area where the power of the computer can easily be demonstrated. As soon as a data set becomes large, a computer becomes an invaluable tool for sorting or finding information you want. Computers are essential to people who work with large data sets.

A computer is recommended for the remaining activities in this investigation. For this session, you can schedule pairs of students to work at the computer over a period of several days while you are waiting for everyone to finish collecting their cat data. Students can work at their own pace at the times you designate. See the Teacher Note, *About data bases* (page 53).

If you have a large demonstration monitor available, you can show the whole class how to browse through the data base, how to sort the data base by a particular characteristic (such as age), and how to search for a particular set of cats (such as all cats with tails shorter than 11 inches, or all cats that are black). If you do not have a demonstration monitor, plan to work with one group or pair of students at a time to get them started. Identify students who catch on quickly and designate them as "data base experts" who are available to give other students assistance. Please be sure to include some girls as experts.

Hand out copies of Student Sheet 4, *Browsing in the data base*, which gives some sample questions to guide your students' exploration of the data base. Alternatively, mount a copy of Student Sheet 4 on cardboard and keep it at the computer station for student reference. ■

✐ TEACHER NOTE
About data bases

We consult data bases often, although we don't always think of them in that way. The telephone book, your own address book, the classified ads, a dictionary, a class list—all of these are forms of a data base. A box of index cards with your students' reading records on them, your grade book, the IEPs (individualized education programs) for some of your students—each is a system for storing data that makes record-keeping easier for you. Any template designed to collect and store information provides a data base.

Computers have made a big difference in the ways we record and handle information, and the cats data base is designed to help your students learn to use the computer as a tool for storing and organizing data. If you do not have access to a computerized data base that you can use in these lessons, develop another system of record-keeping with your students. The information about cats can be written on index cards or on individual data sheets, or (preferably) entered into a computer data base. Before you begin the investigation, you will need to decide what method you'll use for exploring these data.

In the Session 2 activities designed for browsing in the data base, your students will discover how to order the data in some fields (e.g., tail length, age); how to sort data (e.g.,

black fur); and how to manipulate data (e.g., finding the middle-sized tail).

With only 24 cats, it isn't so hard to use file cards or sheets of paper to explore the data. But as we add more and more cats, keeping track of so much information becomes more difficult. A data base on a computer can store a lot of information, and it lets you find what you want quickly. For example, to find the cat named Charcoal, you can use a computerized data base to find Charcoal extremely quickly instead of sorting through all the cards yourself. If you want to see how many cats have green eyes, you can ask the computer for the green-eyed cats, and the sort is done rapidly.

Using a computer allows your students to add the new cat data quickly as they collect it. They can enter the data individually and immediately begin to play with the expanded sample.

We recommend keeping students' data separate from the original cats file so that you have the option of comparing the two samples or merging them into one larger sample of cats. A good computer data base will allow you to merge two files. It's possible that you will want to keep cat data in three files—one for each set of data (those provided and those your students collect) and one with all the data merged. ■

SESSION 3 ACTIVITIES

Entering new data: Getting it all together

☞In this session, students enter their new cat data into the data base. If they are using the computer, you will need to schedule student work as an independent activity. If you do not have a computer, see the alternative activity for this session.

Today you're going to enter your new cat data into the data base. First we'll agree on what procedures to follow, and then you'll work independently. Our goal is to get all of your new data into a form to share with the entire class.

If you have a computer data base: Students' new information will be entered into a separate, new data base so that it can be analyzed separately from the original sample. Have each pair enter their information onto the same data disk, in this second data base. Set up the fields in advance, allowing sufficient space for the data to be entered. Print out a blank copy of the data base to help your students see what's needed when it's their turn to enter their data.

Arrange time for students to make their entries. They often work best in pairs. It takes 10–15 minutes for each student to enter data accurately and save them. If your students are familiar with procedures for entering data, it will take less time; if they are unfamiliar with data bases, it may take longer.

When all the new data have been entered, copy the data base onto additional disks, or print a copy of the new cat data for each group.

Alternative activity: For those without a computer

If you do not have access to a computer: Students bring in their new cat data on Student Sheet 4. One way to make the new data available to the whole class is to provide a large sheet of chart paper divided into columns to match the data base fields. Ask students to enter their data on this large sheet.

After students have entered their data on the chart, collect their data sheets so you have one complete copy of the original data.

When the students need to work with these data in Session 3, you can cut up the chart into strips of data and hand them out to the groups according to the attribute each group is analyzing (that is, give the data strip on age to the group who analyzed the cats' ages before; give the fur-color data strip to those who analyzed that attribute before; and so on).

Alternatively, you might duplicate all the individual data collection sheets for your students' cats and hand out a packet to each group for analysis in Session 4.

After analyzing the new data in Session 3, students will be asked to combine them with the first sample of cats and analyze the whole collection as a new, larger sample. File cards or individual data sheets for each cat will make that task simpler, as students can physically merge the original cat cards with the cards or sheets of new data. ■

Cat's name: Alexander
Gender: male
Age: 18 years
Weight: 11 pounds
Body length: 21 inches
Tail length: 11 inches
Fur color: brown and black stripes, some white
Eye color: green
Pad color: black
Other: Alex's favorite foods are vanilla ice cream and bacon, which he will steal off the table.

SESSION 4 ACTIVITIES

Working with the new cat data: Do our descriptions change?

When you worked with the cat data in the first sample, you said that a typical cat was [read the class's previous conclusions]. Today we'll analyze your new cat data to see whether they lead you to different conclusions. Then we'll look at what happens when you combine these two small samples into one larger sample.

Ask the working groups to analyze the new cat data, using the same characteristic they looked at in Session 1. They may want to make quick sketch graphs or line plots of their new data.

If you have enough computers, small groups can work at them simultaneously. If they must share, schedule their computer time throughout the day.

Classrooms without computers will be using strips from the large data chart or copies of all the individual data collection sheets for this activity.

Analyzing the data: Thinking about new summaries

When the groups have finished their analyses, call the class together and ask what the new sample by itself shows us about cats. Is the typical cat the same? What characteristics change with the new data?

Looking at a much larger sample: Combining smaller samples

What happens when we combine these two small samples?

Ask groups to combine their data from the two samples and to describe the new results. This can be done by merging the computer data base files or by physically adding the sheets of new data to the original cat cards.

Do you see yet another picture of the typical cat now that you've combined these two small samples?

Write the new description of "the typical cat" on the chalkboard.

Reflecting on the sample: How closely does it approximate the population?

How closely do you think this larger sample represents the population of cats? Do you have better data when you combine these two small samples? How could you improve it further?

Remind your class of the description of cats in *Wilson's Book of Mammals*, provided at the start of this investigation (page 48). Do their data show something different? Why might there be differences? How do your students think the data given in Wilson's book were collected?

If you were to continue this study of cats, how could you get even better information? What would you set up as a sampling plan for cats?

Encourage your students to think about ways of sampling a population of cats. Point out that the populations they can easily sample may not be as extensive as they initially think. That is, they may be sampling only "domestic cats in our town" or "domestic cats in our community" rather than "cats."

Extensions

▼ Some classes might enjoy extending their data collection activities into studies of themselves. After collecting information about members of the class in a data base, they can analyze their data to decide what's typical of their class. They might like to compare their data with data from other schools, if available. One class sent a booklet summarizing their data to their pen pal class. They sent copies of their data base, their graphs of the collected data, and their summary statements about themselves. They were careful to describe their data in such a way that people weren't left out—that meant very full, rich descriptions of their results. ("More than half of the kids in the class like to play football, but some are really involved in soccer, and three like to play softball. One kid loves tennis most, and she's the only one who likes it the best.")

▼ Scientists identify and study endangered species with sampling techniques. Upper elementary students are intrigued with learning more about these real-life techniques. Bird banding and bird counts are two ways of estimating the size of the bird population; the Audubon Society or other bird-watching groups in your area may participate in the census of certain species, particularly if they are endangered. Perhaps a member of such a group would be willing to talk to your class.

Most animal studies rely on sampling. Your students may want to learn more about it. *The Voyage of the Mimi* (Sunburst, 1988) is a middle-grades curriculum that uses videotapes and computer software to follow an expedition of scientists into the Atlantic Ocean to study humpback whales. Part of their study involves conducting a whale count. ■

ADVERTISING DECISIONS

  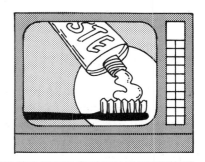

INVESTIGATION OVERVIEW

What happens

Students decide when to advertise a hypothetical new product on television by finding out which shows will be watched by the target audience. They select a sample of the school population, collect television-viewing data, and make recommendations about the placement of the television ads.

The activities take three class sessions of about 45 minutes each. New data must be collected outside of class between Sessions 1 and 2. The timing of Sessions 2 and 3 depends on the size and complexity of the data set your class collects. You may need to depart from the outline presented here.

What to plan ahead of time

▼ Before starting this investigation, alert colleagues to the fact that your students may want to interview some of their students about television-viewing habits.

▼ Provide materials for data collection—clipboards, paper, pens, pencils (after Session 1).

▼ Provide materials for recording and presenting data. Include materials for presentation graphs if your students wish to make them (Sessions 2 and 3).

Important mathematical ideas

Defining a question to be researched. Most research questions are complicated, and the researchers must define the question carefully. The ambiguities built into the central problem in this investigation allow for different interpretations. Encourage extensive discussions as your students define and refine their questions.

Understanding that sampling is used in the real world. This simulation demonstrates some of the ways in which taking and analyzing samples can inform decisions in the business world. Studying a sample provides the opportunity to learn more about a real population.

Developing a sampling plan for a population. Plans for finding representative samples must be carefully developed if they are to reflect the population as accurately as possible. Although some uncertainty is always a part of statistics, sampling is a good way to find out about a population when the population cannot be counted.

Interpreting results of the study. Your students' discussion of the implications of these results is crucial. What do the results mean? What do your students recommend, based on their study? ■

SESSION 1 ACTIVITIES

Introducing the problem: How can we find out about television viewing?

Set the scene for this investigation with the following simulation:

Imagine that you've been asked to give marketing advice to an advertising agency. Its client is a company that has produced a new construction toy. This toy will create rockets, doll houses, robots, furniture for teddy bears and other stuffed animals—all completely designed by the user. The toy appeals mostly to 6- to 11-year-olds. The Construct-a-Toy Company can afford only three television ads.

Your job is to inform the advertising agency when to air their three television ads so that they will pick up the greatest amount of business. What will you do in order to develop your recommendations? They have a limited budget—they'll only pay for you to take a sample of up to 100 people.

Support an open-ended discussion of the situation before the students start to shape a plan for their research. Students enjoy talking about how advertisers make decisions, and some of your students may bring some background information to the discussion. Be prepared for students to raise questions—for instance, are there budget limits? Can they air all three ads during the same show?

Defining the question: What do we want to find out?

Help your students focus on what information they will want to base their decisions on. Certainly they will want to learn something about the television-viewing habits of 6- to 11-year-olds. What, precisely, will they want to learn? What other information might be useful? What do they need to know in order to make their recommendations? What kind of data will be involved? For some ideas about this, see the Dialogue Box, *What do we need to know?* (page 60).

Write on the chalkboard the information your class decides to gather. Help your class focus on the questions they will be asking.

How can you construct questions that get at the information you want? Spend 5 minutes in your small groups and come up with one or two questions that you believe are clear.

After 5 minutes, ask each of the small groups to read their questions aloud. Next ask the class to refine and clarify their questions. Remember to encourage open-ended questions that generate useful information. Questions such as, "What is your favorite TV show?" generate more information than "Which do you like best— 'The Cosby Show' or 'Full House'?"

Before you go out to do your interviews, we'll pilot test your questions in the classroom, to see whether they give you useful information.

Divide the class into pairs and have them collect data from each other. Did problems come up that they hadn't anticipated?

Did anything come up during the pilot test that was a problem? Is the wording of the questions clear? Was everything clear? Did anyone not have a favorite TV show? Did anyone not watch TV?

Refine the questions again, if you need to, and record them on the board or a large piece of chart paper.

Developing a sampling plan: Choosing the sample

What's the population you are looking at? You need to select a sample. Working in small groups, you will have 10 to 15 minutes to come up with a suggestion for a sampling plan. Then we'll all talk about the plan and make a decision about what's the "best" way to get the data you need.

Circulate around the room to observe students' ideas and interactions. When the groups are ready, have them briefly present their sampling plans and the reasons behind them. Then ask the class to discuss and decide on one sampling plan. It could be a mixture of key elements from each group plan. See the Dialogue Box, *Is our sample representative?* (page 61), and the Teacher Note, *Sampling and surveys* (page 62) for more ideas and information.

Record the sampling plan on the board in a place where it can be kept for reference.

Developing a plan for data collection: Who, when, where?

Now that you know whom to ask, you need to decide about the details. Who will go where? How many will each one ask? Will you work in groups? In pairs?

This discussion may be brief. Develop a procedure for asking questions and recording data as they are collected. Role playing may help. The class may need to check schedules with your colleagues to arrange a time for interviews. Be certain that your students know when their data are due to be brought in to the class.

Session 2 should be scheduled after all the data have been collected. You may want to allow one or two days between Sessions 1 and 2. ■

66 99 DIALOGUE BOX
What do we need to know?

This class is collecting data about television viewing. While the students make suggestions about what they need to find out, the teacher records their ideas on the board.

PETER: I think we need to look at what kind of commercials kids enjoy.

MARY LOU: What time you watch TV is important.

ETHLYN: Knowing what stations kids watch would help us.

BRIDGET: I don't agree with these. I think we need to know what are the most watched TV shows. The other stuff won't help us make a decision.

Say more about that, Bridget.

BRIDGET: Well, it's important to know which TV shows they watch and get the ads on popular shows if we can.

BETTINA: And we weren't asked to make the commercial, so we don't need to know what commercials kids like.

How are the rest of you thinking about this?

TAM-SENG: I think it's important to look at when parents and kids watch TV together. If you want them to buy the toy, you make sure the parents see the ad, too.

MANUEL: Yeah, because if the parents don't know about it, the kids can have trouble getting enough money.

It sounds like you're close to formulating your questions. Does anyone have a new idea?

MARIAN: I think if we just ask what shows they watch on television and then ask what shows they watch with their parents, we'll get close.

KIMBERLEY: I go along with Marian. If we find that out, we can make a decision about maybe one ad for just kids and two for parents, or like that.

ISAAC: I think so too.

[*The class reaches a consensus.*]

Let's be clear, then. You want to know two things. Can you find out what you want with two questions? What are you going to say to people?

BILLY: Ask them what they watch on TV.

SARAH: That's too long. We don't want to know everything they watch.

BILLY: Oh, yeah. So ask them what their top five shows are.

PETER: Can we ask five when we want three?

BILLY: Oh. So ask them what their top three shows are.

KELLEY: And when they watch with their parents.

It sounds as though there are two questions. How could you phrase them?

The class works at phrasing the two questions precisely as the teacher records them on the board, erasing and inserting words as the students make suggestions. They end up with these two interview questions:

1. What are the three television shows you watch most?

2. What are the three television shows you watch most with your parent or parents?

After reaching this point, they go on to discuss how to record the information and whom to include in the sample. ■

66 99 DIALOGUE BOX
Is our sample representative?

How will you pick your sample?

BEVERLY: Not seventh graders. They're too old for toys.

GREG: I know some seventh graders pretty well and I think a lot of them play with toys.

BEVERLY: But the toy company wants to know about 6- to 11-year-olds.

KIMBERLEY: We should take kids who are those ages.

Do you want to take kids from school for the sample? Or could you do other things?

SARAH: We can ask brothers and sisters, but there aren't enough, I bet.

JOSEF: It's easier to take kids from the school.

So whom do you want to include?

RICHARD: If we take four kids from one first grade and four from the other and four from the other, and then four kids from the second grade and four from the two others, and four kids from each of the third grades, and four from the fourths, and four from us, and four from Mr. Julian's class, and four from Ms. Jones, then we'll have 60 kids.

BETTINA: I disagree. There aren't enough of each age and we don't go by grade, we go by age.

GREG: We can try to take kids by age when we ask them and we can take 60 kids.

What's the population of kids you want to know about? Remember, this ad agency wants to know about kids in the whole country.

SARAH: We're only good for kids in this part of the country. Can we say that to them?

BENJAMIN: Yeah, we're only good for this school or this area. I think we should get as big a sample as we can, so we need to interview 100 kids. If we divide that up, we get about four kids each. We could do it in groups and make sure we get enough kids for each age.

Let's think about that. Do you want to be sure that there are equal numbers for each age?

KELLEY: We should make sure there's some kids from each age or else we don't really have a fair sample. Like if we go out during a softball game and ask, we don't get a fair sample.

Is there a way you could get a fair sample? What if you go out and wait for the buses to come in the morning and ask the first four kids off each bus?

EMILIO: That's not fair. You get the little kids then. No big kids. And what about walkers?

OK, so what will you do?

MARY LOU: Go to the classes but ask kids their ages, and when we come back and write all the stuff down, we should write it by age.

Are you comparing the ages, or do you just want to be sure you have some of each?

YOLANDA: Oh! We don't need to know how many of each age for the company. They just want to know where to put the ads. So we just don't need to tell them about the ages. But can we get them anyhow? Because I think it's different and I want to see the results.

☞ These students seemed to want to collect data in order to compare the various ages. The teacher had to bring them gently back to the question at hand—the favorite television programs of the 6- to 11-year-olds. The topic was of such compelling interest that students continually brought in other information. The teacher kept them focused on the topic without forcing them to solve the problem in a particular way.

When the students developed their sampling plan, they were very pleased with it. They decided to collect information from other students when they were on their way out to recess rather than interrupt classes. Each data collection team specialized in one classroom and collected data from four students, asking their ages along with the survey questions. ■

✎ TEACHER NOTE
Sampling and surveys

Your students may suggest that they do surveys without sampling a population. This confusion is very common.

When a population is being studied, a carefully defined sample is selected. It is chosen to approximate the population as closely as possible, in miniature. So, for instance, a large sample of families is chosen as Nielsen families (so-named because the Nielsen Company does the sampling). Their homes are hooked up electronically to a data collection center, and information about their television viewing is collected each week. The company reports each week about what shows were watched most and least. Because the Nielsen sample was carefully selected to be representative, advertisers assume that their results are an indication of the habits of the television viewing population of the United States. Because of this accuracy, advertisers are very interested in the weekly figures (as are others, such as program directors and network television officials).

Using a survey to gather data from such a carefully selected sample is different from just surveying an available group. The results of a group survey are certainly helpful—but the results are limited to that group. Unfortunately, how the data were collected is not always reported, so people often incorrectly generalize from a survey,

assuming that the people surveyed constitute a representative sample of the population being studied. It's not always true.

Think of a sample as a shortcut to knowing about a population. We try to get a sample that's as much like the population as possible, that approximates the population without distortion. Statistical formulas and rules about finding sample size and about other sampling procedures have been developed with that in mind. There's always going to be some uncertainty built in, but when the sampling procedures and rules are followed there's a high probability that the results will be reflective of the population under scrutiny. Your students' experiences in selecting samples will prepare them for learning more formal statistical techniques later on.

Stay alert to the possibility that your students may confuse collecting data from selected samples of a population with conducting a simple survey of an available group. Although the act of data collection is similar, the analysis and generalizability are very different. As an analogy, a sample is like a particular shape that is put in front of a bright light. It throws on the wall a larger shape, that is similar to it in every way (you could demonstrate this with an overhead projector). We hope that the large shape is the shape of the distribution of the attribute in the population. If we've selected carefully, it will be close. But there's no way to make it perfectly correct. ∎

SESSION 2 ACTIVITIES

Recording data: Merging the groups' data

You now have all of your data about the television-viewing habits of 6- to 11-year-olds. How can we put them all together?

Figuring out how to organize and record these data will take some time. Students have found a variety of ways of displaying all their data. In one classroom, students recorded the television shows along a horizontal axis and then recorded data in a bar graph with frequency on the vertical axis. In another class, students listed the television shows and made a tally for each piece of data. Another group decided to record each piece of data on a stick-on note; those were then used to create a bar graph of the data. There are many other approaches. Encourage your students to agree on a method that allows them all see the results at once.

If you have asked more than one question (like the class in the Dialogue Box, *What do we need to know?*, page 60), the students will need to find a way to simultaneously display the results on both issues.

Be sure to keep the group's original data as collected. You may want to refer to it when you look back at the results later.

☛ You can either stop here or go on to talking about the results, depending on how long the first part of the session has taken.

Looking at the results: What can we see?

What can you see, now that your data are all entered? How would you describe the results of your data collection? What do you know now? Are you surprised at anything, or are the results what you thought they would be?

Encourage students to talk about what they can see in these data. There may be very clear-cut results, or there may not. This discussion may be fairly brief, or it may raise questions. Support students' questions and help them draw reasonable conclusions. ∎

SESSION 3 ACTIVITIES

Analyzing the results: Making recommendations to the company

Ask students to look again at the results of their survey, and look again at the questions they were to answer for the Construct-a-Toy company.

Spend some time in your small groups deciding what recommendations we should make to the toy company. Think about our results, our data, and the ways we collected our data. Spend 10–15 minutes talking about your recommendations. One person in each group should jot down your recommendations and some of your reasons for them.

Circulate among the groups as they develop their recommendations. Remind them of the original task and the questions they are answering. Focus them on the data if they drift away from them. What can they say with great confidence? Which recommendations are a bit more tentative?

When all the groups are ready, ask them to share their thinking with the whole class. As they report, encourage them to ask about areas that differ from group to group.

You all are interpreting the same data, but you may reach some different conclusions. Talk about your differences and try to understand how another group reached a different conclusion.

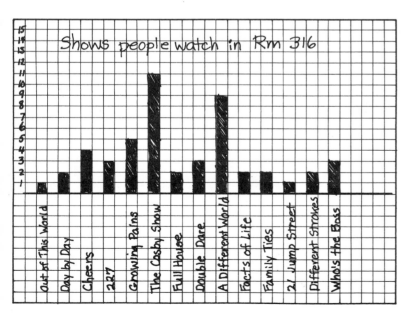

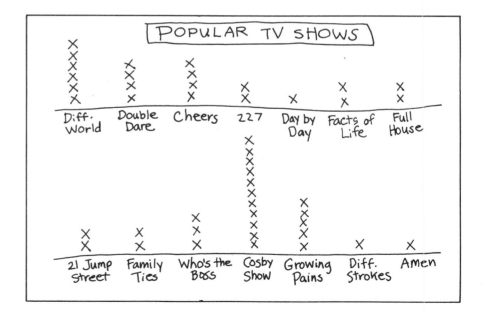

When the groups have finished, ask them to compare their recommendations, come to some conclusions about a group recommendation, and record their final decision on the board or a large piece of chart paper. They should qualify their recommendation, based on their sampling plan.

Broadening the sample

We need to think for a minute about the sampling plan before we leave this investigation. Do you think it was representative? Of what population? If you had more money from the advertiser, and wanted to do an even better job, how would you change or broaden the sample?

Help students look at what a different sampling plan might involve in order to be truly representative of the population of 6- to 11-year-olds.

Extensions

▼ Encourage your students to write a letter to the Construct-a-Toy company, detailing their research study. They might include the original question, their sampling plan, a diagram or graph of the data they collected, and their recommendations. Everything they put in the letter should reflect the connection between their recommendations and the data they collected.

▼ Some of your students may want to develop further the Construct-a-Toy advertising campaign. Designing the toy itself, planning commercials, videotaping those commercials, and developing a marketing strategy are very engaging projects for upper elementary students. Encourage them to learn more about the advertising industry by interviewing local television stations and by reading about it.

▼ If you have students who are concerned about commercials ("There are too many commercials on my favorite show!"), they might like to know about Action for Children's Television. This nonprofit child advocacy organization is concerned about television commercials geared at children. Your students can find out more by writing to Action for Children's Television, 20 University Road, Cambridge, MA 02138. ■

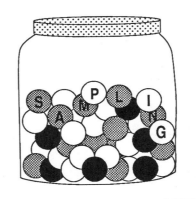

Statistics:
Prediction and
Sampling

PART 3
Solving problems with sampling

A note on the final projects

Two final projects are suggested here. You may do both, but most teachers have selected the one that best fits their situation and the interests of their students.

The first project focuses on play injuries, collecting data to analyze patterns in injuries students have suffered when playing. Some classes have limited this to injuries on the school grounds; others have looked more broadly at playgrounds in the neighborhoods or at specific types of injuries, such as bicycle injuries. If your students enjoy protecting others, this is a good project for them. Their findings can be reported to other classes and might serve as the basis for real change.

The second investigation focuses on data collected from television. After discussing national crime statistics, students watch television to find whether the types of crime in television shows are representative of the profile of crime in the country. If your students enjoy projects involving social issues, this may be very appealing to them. The discussions provoke a good deal of thought and can be the basis for some powerful action.

Both of these projects deal with safety issues. Upper elementary grade students typically are fascinated with safety and respond well to studying aspects of safety. They enjoy knowing about how to protect and care for themselves and for others.

☞ If there is a local issue that you know is important to your students and that lends itself to a study through sampling a population, you may prefer to substitute it for either of these projects. ∎

RESEARCHING PLAY INJURIES

INVESTIGATION OVERVIEW

What happens

Students find out about play injuries in their school or area by collecting statistics from a sample that they define. They then look for patterns in the data and use their findings to take action. Working on a relatively long-term project like this allows them to experience all of the stages of statistical exploration: defining the question and the sample, testing and refining the question, collecting and recording data, and looking for patterns and developing theories.

The activities may take four class sessions of about 45 minutes each, varying with the interest of your class and your own preferences. One plan is to introduce the investigation and help students define the question in the first session. After some trial out-of-class data collection, students refine their questions and develop a sampling plan

in the second session. They then need more out-of-class time to collect data according to their plan. In the final two sessions, they consider the data and make final recommendations based on those data. Although students work in small groups most of the time, they are periodically called together to report about their findings.

These sessions are approximate. Some teachers prefer to spend more time on establishing methods and measurement techniques at the start. Others spend one extra session on the final presentation of the data. You will find natural breaks in the activities and can decide your own best pace.

What to plan ahead of time

▼ Provide materials for data collection and display—graph paper, pens, pencils,

stickers, or stick-on notes (Sessions 1–4).

▼ Provide calculators for use in data analysis (especially Sessions 3 and 4).

▼ Provide computers and graphing or data base software for record-keeping and data analysis (optional, Sessions 2–4).

Important mathematical ideas

Experiencing all the phases of data analysis. Students work on a data collection problem that allows them to make decisions just as other researchers must. They work to define, refine, analyze, and present the results of their work. These experiences help them better understand graphs and other presentations of data. Data collection, display, and analysis in a sustained investigation like this one is somewhat different from that which took place during the short-term investigations earlier in this unit. The Teacher Note, *Phases of data analysis: Learning from the process approach to writing* (page 73), describes the steps involved.

Defining the question. The first phase in data analysis is defining the question and deciding what data are needed to answer it. Encourage discussion about what the question means: When you talk about play injuries, what do you want to look at?

Determining an appropriate sampling plan. Students have to decide how they will take a sample that's representative enough to allow them to make some statements about the incidence of play injuries in the school (or in another population, as they decide).

Looking for patterns in the data. Finding patterns in data lies at the heart of data analysis. When data are presented and re-presented, viewed and re-viewed, researchers find new ways of seeing and analyzing them. Your students may find some very interesting patterns; they may find some exciting ways of analyzing their data. One small-group discussion is included in the Dialogue Box, *Finding patterns in the data* (page 74).

Building theories based on data. When students understand their data and present them clearly, they can then go on to build theories and to develop stories based on their data. The patterns that students may find in

this investigation present a good opportunity for storytelling and theory-building. Your role is to support and encourage this kind of expression.

Making a report. Many students find writing about a mathematical experience to be very challenging and satisfying. Writing about mathematics needs to be encouraged, since it provides both an avenue for creative expression and a way to express mathematical concepts in "plain language." Some students find it easy to write about presentation graphs; others find it difficult. The reports or summaries can be fairly short, but should contain thoughtful treatment of both the mathematical content and the interpretation of data. ■

SESSION ACTIVITIES

Considering the problem: Researching play injuries

In this investigation, your challenge is to become researchers studying one problem in depth. You will use all of your statistical tools to study one area.

I have a hunch that there may be some patterns in the ways you have been injured when you were playing. Have any of you been hurt when you were playing? This can be either at home, or at school, or at a park, or anywhere that you play.

This question will provoke some lively discussion. Fifth and sixth graders love to trade gory stories about their injuries. For some possible repercussions of this discussion, see the Teacher Note, *Sensational issues in the classroom* (page 72). After they have told some of their stories, they will relax and begin to look at broader issues. Be aware that it may take a while to get to the statistical question as this discussion of injuries takes place.

What if we could find some patterns? Say we found that many of you had gotten hurt in a specific place or at a specific time. What is done with research like this?

In one Massachusetts school, the principal studied the playground accident reports and found that most of the injuries on the monkey

bars were to children in third grade and lower. Their hands were too small to grip the bars well. In one fifth and sixth grade class in New York, the students talked with the principal and recommended changes in the way the playground was used and monitored, because they found some locations on the playground that they believed contributed to school-based play injuries.

Defining the question: How can you ask for data?

In order to collect information for a study of play injuries, what would you need to know?

Your students may have some theories they want to test: a particular location they want to focus their concerns on, or a specific kind of equipment, or a specific need on their school playground. Help them as they think through what they hope to do. See the Teacher Note, *I wanna do it myself!* (page 75).

Now that you know what you want to look at, what will you ask?

Record proposed questions on the board as students talk, shaping and reshaping questions as further ideas arise. It's important that students learn to check their proposed questions against the information they want to collect.

Will these questions get you what you want? How will someone else hear these questions?

Homework: Preliminary data collection

When the students have agreed on the questions they want to ask, either photocopy a sheet with all the questions or ask students to write them down to take home.

Tonight at home, give someone your sheet of questions. They are to ask you the questions and write down your answers. Bring in the data tomorrow, and we'll figure out how to look for preliminary patterns. Then we'll be ready to define the population you'll study and develop a sampling plan. Next you'll collect the data, study them, and make some action plan.

Bringing in data from home: A preliminary study

Did anyone run into problems with the questions? Were there any surprises?

Allow a little time for your students to talk about their experiences in being the subjects of data collection.

Collecting, recording, organizing, describing, and interpreting preliminary data: Getting it all together

First, let's decide how you can go about putting your data together. Then you'll look at these data for any preliminary patterns.

The question of compiling the data depends

to some degree on their complexity. You may want to recommend that students compile their data in small groups, then share them from group to group (perhaps get them photocopied) so that each group can compile everyone's data. Alternatively, your class may be able to record all their data on the chalkboard and copy them as they work in their small groups.

Encourage students to use quick sketch graphs to avoid getting overinvolved with detail. For a typical discussion, see the Dialogue Box, *Finding patterns in the data* (page 74). When groups are finished, ask them to share what they found in these data.

What can you see in our data? What can you say about your injuries? Are there patterns in these preliminary data? What might such patterns mean?

If there are patterns, spend some time discussing what implications they might have for the rest of the study. Your students may want to develop some hypotheses about whether they think these will be true of a larger population. Is this class a representative sample of the whole school?

☞ Throughout this investigation, we assume that your students will want to study the population of students in their school. However, that assumption is merely made for ease in describing the activities. If your class is researching a different population, simply substitute its name wherever we mention the school population.

Refining the question and developing a sampling plan

Think about where to go from here. Do you need to change any of the questions? How will you select a representative sample? How do you want to proceed after the sample is chosen?

Your students have experience in developing a sampling plan, in refining questions, and in organizing data collection procedures. Help them think through their plans. Focus particularly on the sampling plan, continually asking students how their proposed sample is representative of the population they are researching.

How does this sample of students represent everyone in the school? Will you feel comfortable making claims about everyone? Are you sure everyone had a fair chance to be in the sample?

Do some role playing with them before they collect data so that they will know where to go, whom to interview, and what to ask.

Wait until data are collected before scheduling the next session. The process may take two or three days, depending on your data collection plan.

Collecting, organizing, and analyzing data: What can we see in the sample?

As students return to the classroom with their data on play injuries, compile the results in a way that allows everyone easy access to the data. If you have skilled computer users, this is a good time to print out a data base. Otherwise, find a way to duplicate the data for the working groups. If students record information one question at a time, they may be able to begin graphing and charting information quite rapidly, even before all the information is recorded.

Work in your groups today to record and organize these data. Make some quick sketch graphs so that you can begin to analyze the information you have gathered. Later you will be identifying any problems you see and making recommendations about safety.

Help students spend time in teasing out patterns in the data, looking at the implications of any patterns they find, and beginning to develop theories based on the results of their study.

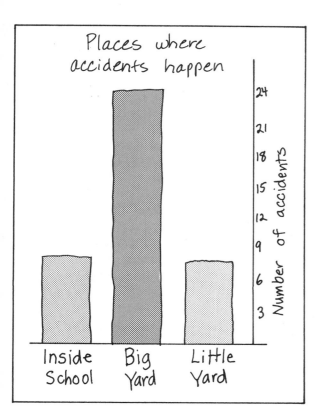

Places where accidents happen

Number of accidents

24
21
18
15
12
9
6
3

Inside School   Big Yard   Little Yard

Making predictions about a population: What is true, based on the sample?

You've looked at results from a sample. If these findings are true for the sample, what would you say about the population? What claims might you make?

Encourage your students to extrapolate from the sample to the population. Given these data and these results, what might be true? What do they not know for sure?

Developing theories: What have we found?

You will be making recommendations based on your data and your findings. How can you describe your results?

In the whole class, have the groups report about their findings. Record those for everyone to see. Then spend some time spinning theories about the data. Challenge students to support their theories with data.

Making recommendations for action: What needs to be modified?

We've looked at the results now. What recommendations would you make that might alleviate some of the problems you've identified? Make a list of those recommendations, and let's see if we all agree about them.

Is there any action that grows naturally out of these explorations? This could be writing a letter to the school administration, writing a letter to a local newspaper, writing an article for the local paper—or writing to a manufacturer, or a health and safety organization. Students can find a variety of civic groups and government offices that use the kind of information they have gathered to make policy. See the Teacher Note, *Making final presentations* (page 76).

If students have policy recommendations, they could be encouraged to decide how to make those known to others. If, for instance, they find that second graders are at risk for bicycle injuries, they might want to generate some safety programs for second graders and to write a newsletter to parents that warns them about the increased likelihood of bicycle injury. The Dialogue Box, *Making a presentation about safety* (page 77), shows how one class took their ideas to the school principal.

Ages of injured

			X					
			X					
			X		X			
			X		X			
			X	X	X			
			X	X	X			
			X	X	X			
		X	X	X	X	X	X	
	X	X	X	X	X	X	X	
X	X	X	X	X	X	X	X	X

4   5   6   7   8   9   10   11   12

Age of injured person

Publishing findings

You have the opportunity now to make your findings known by publishing them. In your groups, write a summary of the study and support it with graphs and charts of information. Including the data will strengthen your case. Talk about your sample and how it represents the population.

Writing about the project can be inspirational to some of your students. This final step will involve making presentation graphs and working out a summary description of the study. Be sure that each report includes a discussion of the sampling plan.

Thinking about the data: Is further information needed?

If students decide that they want to pursue the topic further, encourage them to refine and develop their information. This exploration could become a long-term project; the decision is theirs and yours. ■

✎TEACHER NOTE
Sensational issues in the classroom

Ten- and eleven-year-olds have always loved being graphic about horrible accidents or terrible events that have befallen them. If you ask them to talk about play injuries, they are likely to fling themselves into a "can-you-top-this" kind of discussion.

One of the reasons for such interest is that many students do not believe that they can be seriously injured. They feel invulnerable. On the other hand, they know intellectually that terrible things happen. They may live in a neighborhood that has serious crime; they may know someone who lost a family member to violence. They may have experienced the loss of a family member or friend through an accident. Typically, however, these early adolescents are fascinated with accidents and the details.

Students at this age need to develop a sense of what to do if there's a serious accident—they love to know about first aid treatments and want very much to be able to cope in an emergency. They also like to know that they are getting old enough to know how to protect others. Doing research about a safety issue puts them in the front lines, protecting others (young children or vulnerable animals are good candidates for protection).

Because of their need to feel efficacious, fifth and sixth grade students enjoy studying a problem that has real life consequences, and about which they can take some action. Studying play injuries can lead to real changes on the playground, in the park, or at home. If these changes can be geared to protecting younger children, so much the better.

The "blood and guts" kind of discussion can be a way in to this concern. The teacher's role in such a discussion is delicate. You can certainly focus on the safety aspects of the accidents, asking questions like these:

What time of day was it?

How did you get help in taking care of yourself?

How did you get to the hospital?

In some instances you may prefer to provide the reassurance that students of this age still need from adults, with comments and questions like these:

That's not very likely to occur again. How unusual that it happened.

I'm sure your family is much more careful about boiling water since you got burned.

Bleeding like that is frightening. It's a good thing you stopped it by pressing on the cut.

You may want to turn the discussion away from gore and toward data collection:

How could you record that for our data collection?

Should you count only cuts that needed stitches, like yours did?

What would Bettina write if she were interviewing you?

Such data present a unique opportunity for your students to take an active role in protecting themselves and others. You have an unusual chance to help your students see that research and recommendations based on statistics can be a way to take action in a difficult, complex environment. ■

✎ TEACHER NOTE
Phases of data analysis: Learning from the process approach to writing

The process of data analysis is similar to many other creative processes. Students doing data analysis follow the same processes that adults do; the analyses may be less complex, but the procedures are the same. In data analysis, as in writing or art, teachers help children do real work rather than stilted school assignments requiring fill-in-the-blank responses. The teacher's role is relatively subtle—shaping the process, asking questions that guide the students' progress toward their goals, hearing and responding to their ideas and theories. Students are expected to have something original and interesting to say, and the teacher provides an environment that enriches and supports students' self-expression.

Data analysis has many similarities to the process approach to writing, which typically includes four phases. The process starts with a **planning phase** (often called pre-writing or brainstorming). This is followed by the **writing phase,** when a very rough draft of ideas is first put down on paper. The third phase is the **revision** or **rewriting phase** when the writer elaborates, clarifies, restructures, and edits the piece. The final phase is the **publication phase,** when the

writer's completed piece is shared with others. These processes may be reiterated until the piece of writing is finished.

Data analysis has four phases parallel to those in the writing process:

Phase One: Brainstorming and planning. During this time, students discuss, debate, and think about their research question. In some cases, defining and agreeing upon the question may take a considerable amount of time. Having defined the question and agreed upon terms, students consider possible sources of data, ways of recording them, and how they might organize themselves to collect needed information.

Phase Two: Putting it on paper. Collection and representation of data allows students to develop their "discovery drafts"—what we call "sketch graphs"—the first draft of the information on which they base their developing theories. Students represent the data in a variety of ways to help them describe the important features. They use their first drafts as tools as they look for relationships and patterns in the data.

Phase Three: Revision. Writers are encouraged to share their drafts with their peers in order to determine how an audience perceives their work. Similarly, in the data analysis process, the students often present their sketch graphs, preliminary findings, and beginning theories to their working group in order to see whether their interpretations seem supported by the data, and whether others see things they haven't noticed. Revision in data analysis may include finding new ways to organize and represent the data, developing better descriptions of the data, collecting additional data, or refining the research questions and collecting a different kind of data.

Phase Four: Publication or display. The nature of "publishing" the results of data analysis varies, just as it does for a story or essay. Sometimes students develop a theory that is the basis for a report on a particular topic; at other times they may develop a theory that inspires further investigation. A completed report of a data analysis investigation may involve a written description of the study with conclusions and recommendations, final presentation graphs of information previously displayed in working graphs, and a verbal or written presentation of the report to an interested audience.

When teachers think about the writing process, their role as facilitator and helper seems familiar and obvious. Of course students need time to think and revise their work! Of course they need to be challenged and led, sensitively, to the next level of awareness. The writing process seems more familiar to most of us than the mathematics process because we, too, have done writing.

The process of data analysis needs the same kind of teacher support. Students need to try their ideas, to rough them out, to be challenged and encouraged to go further in

their thinking. It is important that they have time to think and to consider options—and vitally important that they see their work as part of a process. Data analysis, like writing, is not cut and dried. There are many ways to approach a question and many conclusions to be drawn. Like writing, mathematical investigation is a creative blend of precision and imagination. ∎

---

66 99 DIALOGUE BOX
Finding patterns in the data

In this fifth and sixth grade classroom, students have brought in the play-injury data about themselves. They have recorded their injuries, their ages at time of injury, and where the injury occurred. Now they have begun to look at the data with an eye to finding patterns. The small group represented in this dialogue has made a line plot to record number of injuries at different ages. Mary Lou also made a bar graph to record the places the injuries occurred, and Marian made one recording the type of injury (cut, bruise, and so forth).

BILLY: I don't think we have the same information from everyone, because some kids wrote down stuff like simple bruises and scratches that took maybe 30 seconds to get over. I only told about the big stuff.

MARIAN: Yeah, like me when I almost cut off a finger.

MARY LOU: This is something we should complain about and make everybody do it the same.

BILLY: Mr. Stein said we could change the questions later if this didn't work very well.

MARY LOU: But look here—lots of kids were hurt when they were 7.

MANUEL: Well, I think we can look at that. There's a lot more stuff at 7 than at 10.

MARIAN: Look, there's a lot of bike accidents.

MARY LOU: Yeah, like mine. I went around a corner and skidded and fell off my bike and I got sand in my skin and it still shows.

MARIAN: Well, there's a lot of bike stuff.

MANUEL: I just figured out that school, the park, and home are very dangerous.

BILLY: So far we got two things. More 7-year-olds and more bikes.

MARY LOU: What about where it happens? The school has a lot of injuries.

MANUEL: There's a lot of injuries in the playground. We can find something to do about that.

☛ When the students reported back to the whole class, they found that the major issues they had identified agreed with the findings of the other small groups. In the large discussion, they all agreed to focus only on schoolyard injuries so that they could make recommendations for changes. As one of the students said, "I got hurt when I played in that yard. But I don't have to let other kids get hurt, too." ∎

✎ TEACHER NOTE
I wanna do it myself!

When upper elementary students start their own projects in data collection and analysis, they may select questions that you immediately recognize as problematic. It's very tempting to simplify their questions for them, to save them from wrestling with messy data or overwhelming amounts of information. Isn't it important to keep them from being overwhelmed? Shouldn't a teacher help simplify their questions in advance? The answer is no! Their final projects may solicit messy data, but wrestling with messy data is an important part of the analytic process.

Students must struggle with these issues themselves, but teachers have an important role in the process. It is vital that you encourage students to take plenty of time to think about their research questions. What data would help them answer their questions? How can they get those data? After students have collected their data, they must—with your support—carefully consider their results. Are they reasonable? Can they see any patterns in the data? Are there other avenues to take? Messy data are the heart of the process—in fact, most real data are messy. Tidying them up too early will not help students in the long run.

As an example, when students in one sixth grade collected information about play injuries, they ended up with so much data that they could not easily organize and describe them. They concluded that they couldn't make any sense of their results unless they limited the sphere of their investigation. They decided to limit the study to play injuries incurred *at school*. This more focused study allowed them to find patterns in the data, and they were ultimately able to make important recommendations about safety on their own playground. The students were able to make good decisions on their own about how to focus their study *after* their first experiences with their data—and they learned something important about data analysis in the process.

Another typical problem is a collection of data that does not reveal an obvious pattern. For example, students often collect data on favorite things and typically end up with "flat graphs." That is, a survey on favorite ice cream flavor may look like this:

lime sherbet	chocolate	vanilla	peppermint	oreo	orange sherbet	strawberry	raspberry	rocky road	chocolate chip	M & M	coffee
	X				X			X	X	X	
X	X	X	X	X	X	X	X	X	X	X	X

Teachers often see in advance that students will need to categorize their data and may be tempted to suggest categories even before the data are collected: "You're going to get so many different answers. Maybe you just want to select five popular flavors and do your survey with those flavors." However, simplifying the question *ahead of time* may result in less interesting data, as well as lower student interest. After students have collected some data, you can encourage them to reclassify the information: "Can you find ways of reorganizing your results so that you can make some generalizations? If you grouped together all the flavors that include chocolate, are there some patterns?" Statisticians often need to think about reclassifying their collected information as they look for patterns in the data. Rather than signifying a mismanaged investigation, this process lies at the heart of data analysis! ■

✎ TEACHER NOTE
Making final presentations

When students have carefully researched a topic and end up with something to say, it is important that they find a good way of delivering their message. Following are some of the formats available.

Presentation to a responsible official. If your students' work focuses on the school, their presentation might best be directed to the principal and the superintendent of schools. If they made a townwide effort, you might do better with municipal officials. Usually, it's in the best interest of politicians to meet with school children.

Newspaper. The local newspaper may be interested in covering the story if your students have found something that is of general community interest. In one town, students found that the bike path was dangerous, especially for walkers. They studied the accidents reported by students along the bike path and sampled the area around the bike path to find out the kinds of accidents people reported. After they noticed that there were more problems to walkers than to riders, they suggested that the community construct a wide path alongside the bike path in order to keep the two kinds of traffic separate. First they presented their ideas in the school, then to the school board, and finally to the newspaper. Members of the town government were interested and asked

the class to make the presentation to them as well. With each of these presentations, students were careful to present a summary of their methods, their data, and their graphs, charts, and recommendations.

Local television. Your students may be interested in presenting a short segment on a local television station or on the school network. For such a presentation, they might practice in the classroom, videotaping a description of their project and making their graphic data displays large and easily readable. You might make a multi-media presentation if such materials are available to you.

School library. You may find that your students' work lends itself to the creation of a large book or booklet that can be donated to the school library for others to see. Making their work available to others on a long-term basis creates models of statistical research for younger students who may pursue such projects later. You may also find that the town library is interested.

Desktop publishing programs allow your students to generate formal, professional-looking reports with the computer. They enjoy making things look "real," and teachers often find that the promise of real publication is a strong motivator. ■

"DIALOGUE BOX
Making a presentation about safety

The principal of the school has been invited to this sixth grade classroom. The students have studied the incidence of injuries on the playgrounds surrounding the school and have some specific recommendations to improve playground safety.

ETHLYN: What we did was we wondered if there were ways kids hurt themselves in school that we could do something about. So we decided to study it and do research about it.

EMILIO: So we looked at all the kids in the school, and we picked out a sample to use that were some kids from each grade and some kids from each room. We decided to ask them questions, and we went to the rooms and we asked five kids each.

BRIDGET: And we asked those kids, and we wrote stuff down, and then we looked at it. We asked kids when they got hurt playing at school. Where was it, and what were they doing, and how old were they. And we made a lot of graphs and stuff.

BENJAMIN: Here are some of the graphs and some of the facts we found out.

EMILIO: We found 33% of all the injuries happened when kids were running and playing tag. And 55% of all of them

happened when kids were in the back playground.

THE PRINCIPAL: Why do you think that's true?

ETHLYN: Because that's the place that kids like run more, because there's more space. And there aren't so many grownups.

BRIDGET: Anyhow, we have some recommendations to make about it.

TAM-SENG: We think there should be a better schedule for lunch because we share the playground with the junior high. We think if our grades don't go out there at the same time it will be better.

PETER: And we recommended that because the playground was crowded, maybe we could like get the vacant lot that's over there next to the teacher's parking lot, and we could use it for the little kids and put some stuff for them over there.

ALICE: And maybe we need another teacher or some other adult out during recess. Maybe we can get some high school kids to come over here. I made this map of where the accidents happen. Each number is an accident. And we think we need another grownup right here (*points to the upper left corner of her playground map*).

(Dialogue Box continued)

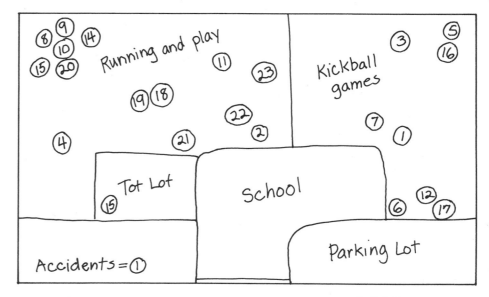

ACCIDENTS IN OUR SCHOOL YARD

THE PRINCIPAL: Can you show me some other information? I want to see how many more injuries happen when students are running.

BENJAMIN: Oh, yeah. Here's the graph. There's lots more.

THE PRINCIPAL: That's very vivid. I could use more data like those when I talk with the teachers about your findings. In fact, I'd appreciate a written report with graphs and your data and your recommendations. Is that possible?

I think people would like to do that.

THE PRINCIPAL: And in the meantime, I want you to think about going around to the younger grades to talk about your findings. If you could help the younger students realize that these injuries can be serious, it would help us a lot.

YOLANDA: And we could explain about what games we think are safe and what ones aren't, couldn't we?

THE PRINCIPAL: Good idea.

☞ The students realized that their findings were being taken seriously, and the principal was able to help them see that their graphs and charts and their recommendations could be combined into one large package of information for the whole school community. These students had achieved an important goal: They had used the process of data collection and analysis to communicate their ideas to others. ■

A STUDY OF CRIME ON TELEVISION

INVESTIGATION OVERVIEW

What happens

Students research television crime by collecting statistics from a sample that they define. They then look for patterns in the data and use their findings to make specific recommendations. In the process, they experience all of the stages of statistical exploration: defining the question and the sample, testing and refining the question, collecting and recording data, and looking for patterns and developing theories.

The point of this study is that crime as portrayed on television is not representative of the overall pattern of crime in the United States. Entertainment programs, news reports, and special events tend to focus on crimes against persons, which are relatively infrequent in comparison with crimes against property. Entertainment shows tend to focus on murder and robbery, both of which are

much less frequent than assault or larceny. Although this investigation certainly touches on some difficult topics, it is a good opportunity for your students to compare their reality with depictions of life on television. The Teacher Note, *Sensational issues in the classroom* (page 72), explores the teacher's role in discussing sensitive topics.

The activities may take four class sessions of about 45 minutes each, depending on the way your class shapes the project. You might introduce the investigation and help students define the question in the first session, before they collect data at home for a preliminary study. Based on these preliminary findings, students might revise their questions and data collection techniques in the second session, then collect further data before the final two sessions, which can be devoted to looking for patterns building theories, and making final recommendations.

Some teachers prefer to spend more time on establishing methods and measurement techniques at the start. Others spend one extra session on the final presentation of the data. You will find natural breaks in the activities and can decide your own best pace.

What to prepare ahead of time

▼ Duplicate Student Sheets 5 and 6 (pages 93-94) for each student, *or* prepare to present them on an overhead projector (Session 1).

▼ Be prepared to duplicate Student Sheet 7 (page 95) or a similar form that students devise themselves for data collection (Session 1, homework).

▼ Obtain the statistics on your local and state crime rates, if possible. Usually the local incidences of crime are reported annually by the city hall or town government. If your town publishes a town or city report, it will be included in that report. There may be a weekly "crime column" in your local newspaper, as well.

State statistics are often recorded in state reports (printed at the end of their fiscal year) or in the *Statistical Abstract of the United States*, put together by the U.S. Bureau of the Census. We have included a data sheet (page 87) with information from the *Statistical Abstract* that gives you the state statistics for 1989 in case you are unable to locate current state data elsewhere.

▼ Consider bringing in a video tape of a TV show to help students establish and clarify their definitions of TV crimes (Session 2).

▼ Provide materials for data collection and display—graph paper, pens, pencils, stickers, stick-on notes (Sessions 1–4).

▼ If your students embark on a very large study, provide calculators for their use in data analysis (especially Sessions 3 and 4).

▼ Provide a computer with graphing or data base software for record-keeping and data analysis. (Optional, Sessions 2–4)

Important mathematical ideas

Experiencing all the phases of data analysis.
Students collect data from television shows and study the incidence of crime portrayed on television. They experience data collection, display, and analysis in this investigation, and work with data in a more sustained way than the earlier short-term investigations. In order to analyze their data they must make decisions about organizing and displaying information for a naïve audience to understand. The Teacher Note, *Phases of data analysis; Learning from the process approach to writing*, (page 73) describes the phases of such an extended investigation.

Defining the question.
When you talk about crime on television, what issues do you want to look into? How do you define crime? How can we analyze what we see on television? These and other questions are addressed in the first phase of this unit as students define the question and decide what data are needed to answer it. Because this is a real-world investigation, discussion and agreement on definitions will take some time.

Determining an appropriate sampling plan.
How can we sample all of the television shows available? Will we all watch the same shows? Sampling a cross section of television shows takes a good deal of agreement and coordination. First students decide on a sample of television shows that will be representative of all television shows. Then they must develop a plan to view those and record information.

Looking for patterns in the data.
Finding patterns in data lies at the heart of data analysis. As students look at the data they collect from television, they may find interesting patterns. Is there more crime after 9:00 PM? Is crime more violent on Saturday morning television?

Building theories based on data.
Patterns in data present an excellent opportunity for theory-building. Why might these patterns appear? How would students explain them? Can they develop theories which encompass more than one pattern? Can they find multiple theories for one pattern? As students engage in this type of analysis, they are engaged in the pieces of creative data analysis that intrigue and delight adult statisticians and scientists. Finding and building theories about data will engage many students in creative mathematical work.

Making a report.
Reporting about the incidence and pattern of crime on television can be a challenging project for your students. Writing about mathematics is still relatively uncommon in elementary school classrooms; it needs to be encouraged and supported in both its creative and mathematical aspects. Reports to the class or to a broader audience (other classes in the school or parent groups may well be interested) tap many aspects of mathematical communication. Such presentations can be informal and may be relatively short, but students can be engaged in thoughtful treatment of both the mathematical content and the interpretation of data. ∎

SESSION ACTIVITIES

Introduction: Doing research

In our unit on sampling, you've learned to use a valuable statistical tool. Your challenge in this investigation is to use sampling and your other data analysis tools as you become researchers studying one problem in depth.

Introducing the study: Setting the scene

What do you think is the most frequent crime in the United States?

Take the students' ideas, and ask for their reasons. Some may say "Murder, because that's what's on the news," or "Cars get stolen because it happens in my neighborhood." Be sure to ask for supporting evidence.

Hand out or display on the overhead projector Student Sheet 5, *Incidence of crime in the United States, 1987.*

Here's a chart that shows you the number of crimes committed in the U.S. in 1987. These figures come from the FBI's report, *Crime in the United States*. What can you see in these data?

Spend some time reading and talking about the data together. Be sure that your students notice that the figures are in thousands.

Which seems to be the most frequent crime? How many times did it happen in 1987? Here's another way to look at it.

Hand out or display Student Sheet 6, the bar graph illustrating these same data.

Spend some time looking at the graph. Ask students to talk about the shape of these data. See the Teacher Note, *The shape of the crime data* (page 85).

Considering the problem: Researching crime on television

From your experience, which crimes are shown most often on television? What would you predict?

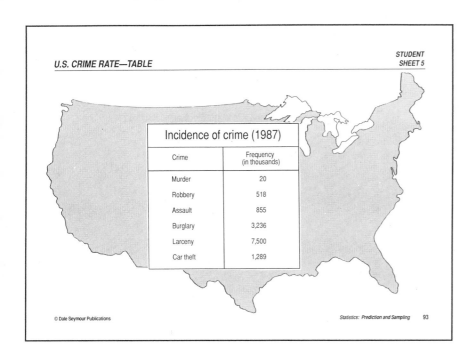

U.S. CRIME RATE—TABLE

STUDENT SHEET 5

Incidence of crime (1987)

Crime	Frequency (in thousands)
Murder	20
Robbery	518
Assault	855
Burglary	3,236
Larceny	7,500
Car theft	1,289

Statistics: Prediction and Sampling 93

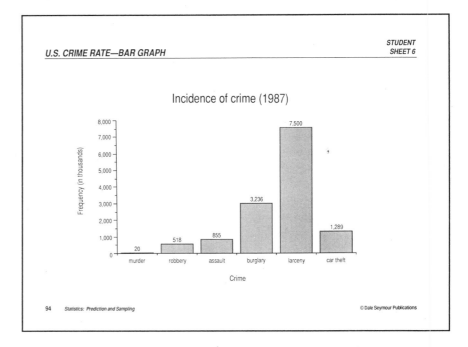

U.S. CRIME RATE—BAR GRAPH

STUDENT SHEET 6

Incidence of crime (1987)

94 *Statistics: Prediction and Sampling*

Ask students to predict, and to talk about reasons for their predictions and their hypotheses. Ask probing questions.

Is television crime like the national statistics? Why? Why not?

You'll be doing a research study on television crime over the next week. As a starting point, let's plan to study the kinds of crimes that television shows us, and compare those with the national crime statistics to see whether TV shows are a representative sample of the kinds of crime in the United States.

You've learned a lot about sampling. This is a good opportunity to look at a population—the population of crimes in the United States—and think about whether what you see on television is a representative sample of that population.

Your students will want to talk about this. Support their early theories and their first ideas as a way of "brainstorming" the problem. Someone will certainly suggest studying TV as a way of finding out more!

Defining the questions: How can you get pilot data?

As you start to study this question, you will be collecting data tonight so that you can test your ideas. How could you collect data about crime on television? In your other studies, you've asked people or used information that someone gave to you. What could you do here?

There are different methods of data collection, and the one that your students will be using in this investigation is observation. Sometimes data are collected through interviews, sometimes through measurement, sometimes through observation, and often through a combination of those methods.

Let's talk a little about how you'd go about watching television for crimes. What should you look for? What should you write down? After you decide on some methods, you'll try them out tonight, and you'll have a chance to refine them tomorrow.

Your students will spend a significant amount of time in defining the observational categories. How will they define a criminal act? What kinds of events will they count? How will they determine what's not really a crime? Will they use the same categories as those in the *Statistical Abstract*?

Your students will need to define and decide which television shows to watch, and over what period of time. When should they watch television? Late afternoon? Evening? Both? Should they watch only crime shows? Should they watch shows they predict will not contain crime? Should they watch the news? See the Teacher Note, *Recording crime data* (page 85).

How will they watch the shows? Will pairs of students record information on specific shows? Should they have more than one

record of the crime events? Often data that are observational, and subject to interpretation, are recorded by more than one observer so that their records can be compared later. Be sure to post the schedule so that your students know what they are responsible for viewing.

After your students have decided what shows to watch, help them to think about how to record the information they may get. You may want to distribute copies of Student Sheet 7, *Recording crime data from TV shows*, which offers one way to record the information. Your students may come up with their own form, or may want to modify this one; if they do, make copies of their recording system for to them.

Homework: Watch TV!

Record your observations tonight, and tomorrow we'll see what kinds of problems you ran into and whether you need to change your definitions or your procedure.

Bringing in the viewing data: A preliminary study

The day that students bring in their data, look at the results of this preliminary study.

What happened when you watched TV for crimes? Did anyone run into problems?

Allow time for them to talk informally about problems. Some of your students will have had difficulties. Some will not have found any crimes at all; some will have had a hard time keeping up with the data collection.

As your students talk about their experiences, listen to their ideas and keep records of what was problematic. Record a list of problems on the chalkboard. You will use this list as a basis for refining the data collection process.

Collecting, recording, organizing, describing, and interpreting preliminary data: Getting it all together

Do you think the crimes you saw on television last night mirror the profile of crimes in the whole country? How can we compare these two sets of data?

Ask students to compile their own data to see whether the general picture of crime they saw on TV is similar or different from the profile of the national crime statistics. The simplest way is to make a huge bar graph on the board, with students making marks or

placing stick-on notes for each instance of crime they observed in a particular category. Your class may have other ideas for pooling their data, however. Help your class come to a consensus about their methods.

Analyzing preliminary data: Was yesterday's TV crime representative of crime in the country?

What can you see in these data? Tell me about the shape of the TV data.

Ask students to look closely at the profile of the crime data from television. What is the most frequent crime shown? What are the relative proportions of the TV crimes?

Compare these results with your graphs of the crime statistics for the United States. Are they similar? Why might they be [alike/different]?

This is a crucial question, the one that guides the students' continuing research. If the television crimes are *not* representative of those of the country as a whole, why would they be different? Students can begin to develop theories. Why are crimes against people so much more frequent on television than crimes against property?

Refining the definitions and developing a viewing plan

You have collected data from only one sample of television shows. That not a very big sample. The next stage of your TV crime

research will involve collecting more data. Spend some time now deciding how to improve your data collection methods or your definitions. Where do you want to improve things?

Collect ideas from the class. Refine the observation instrument as needed, and make copies for student use at home. Collecting data from Saturday morning cartoons and children's TV shows would be interesting. Your students may want to collect data in different categories to see whether the crimes shown on the news, on cartoon shows, and on "regular" television are different. To ensure that they have time to get enough data, give them a few days before scheduling the next class session on this investigation.

Organizing and analyzing data: What do we find?

After your students have brought in their observational data and have recorded them, have them work in small groups to analyze them. Then ask them to share their observations with the rest of the class.

What can you say about these observational data? Are they like the preliminary data you collected? What would you say about how television presents crimes, based on these data?

Predicting to a population: What would the national figures look like if TV were a perfect mirror?

In the whole group, discuss each small group's conclusions. Is TV crime representative of the pattern of national crime? Are the dangers of life in the United States depicted accurately on television?

Why might there be differences? Do your students have ideas about why TV might present a picture that's different from reality?

Making recommendations: Choosing to take action

Sometimes younger children think that life is scary because they see a lot of crime on TV. Sometimes they believe that things like murder and shooting and robbery happen in real life as much as they do on television. What would you say to younger children about that?

Fifth and sixth graders often want to *do something* when they believe that their world is not as fair as they would like it to be. They may want to take action by writing to the television networks, presenting their study, and noting that the TV does not fairly represent the crime pattern in the United States. Students can choose the audience for their final presentation (you might want to include local branches of networks and local cable TV station managers). They might also

publish reports and booklets for their peers. For more detail, see the Teacher Note, *Making final presentations* (page 76).

Upper grade students are typically very interested in taking action in behalf of others. They might want to present their report to the primary grade teachers in the school so that the teachers could talk with the younger students about crime on TV. Perhaps your students will want to make presentations in the younger students' classes, letting them know that the world of crimes against persons on TV is not completely representative of the real world.

Extensions: What are further directions of study?

The data your students collect about crime on TV shows may be the beginning of a larger study of television violence and crime. Many fascinating statistics can be generated by sampling children's TV programs, as well as adult programs in prime time, and recording the number of instances of violence seen in a typical viewing session. This topic is very appealing to upper elementary students and leads them to think about ways of sampling events over time. ■

✎TEACHER NOTE
The shape of the crime data

The crime data presented on Student Sheets 5 and 6 are found in the *Statistical Abstract of the United States: 1989.** Because they are in categorical form, be cautious about how your students describe them (there is no median, for instance, because they do not have an intrinsic order). However, students can still analyze these data; particularly they can compare the relative frequency of different categories in the bar graph.

What can students see? As they look at the data, help them attend to some of the important overall patterns. Larceny is by far the most frequent. How would they describe the relative frequency of larcenies and burglaries? How might they describe the comparison of other categories? Why doesn't murder show up on this bar graph? Does that mean there were no murders?

Your students will want to talk about crimes they have seen or know about. For tips on handling a similar topic, refer to the Teacher Note, *Sensational issues in the classroom* (page 72). There are lots of crimes that aren't listed here. Embezzlement, drug crimes, conspiracy, kidnapping—and more—aren't listed. If your students become fascinated

with these data, help them find a copy of the *Statistical Abstract* and see whether they can develop their own bar graphs using other data on crime rates.

Show them the distinction between crimes against persons and crimes against property, and compare those categories. It reassures many students to know that they are safer than they sometimes think when they watch television, since most criminals want very much to avoid being discovered while committing a crime. ∎

---

* U.S. Bureau of the Census, *Statistical Abstract of the United States: 1989*, 109th edition. (Washington, DC: Government Printing Office, 1989), page 166. These data come from the United States Federal Bureau of Investigation's report, *Crime in the United States (annual edition).*

✎TEACHER NOTE
Recording crime data

This investigation presents some real challenges to students: deciding how to define their question about crime on television, how to identify crimes as they are depicted on television, and then what TV shows to watch and what to record. Fifth and sixth graders are capable of carrying out these activities, in their own ways and at their own levels. Following are some suggestions for making things a little smoother for your class.

Questions to consider. Students need to think about whether they will include only all crimes they *see*, or whether they can include crimes they hear mentioned. If they include only crimes they see, their data will be different, and the incidence of crime will be lower. Should they count murder if they don't see it, but only see the dead body? They will have to decide this issue.

Definitions. What definitions will students use? When someone starts a fist fight, is that an assault? If someone pushes someone else, is that an assault? When is a shoving match an assault, and when is it just jostling someone? Bringing in a videotape of a TV show would give students a chance to practice in the classroom what they will be doing at home and to talk about how they will define the crimes they observe.

Sampling time. If students spend 45 minutes each watching TV, they must record *all* the instances of crime they see in that time. If there is something in a commercial, they will have to make a decision about whether to include it or not. The time spent observing must be defined carefully, and students must be diligent about starting and stopping times for data collection.

Recording data. Keeping up with the flow of data will be hard on some shows. When there is a huge fistfight involving many people, there are a lot of assaults. How should that be tallied? What will students call a shooting where someone is wounded? What will they record if there's a kidnapping?

News coverage of crime brings up a set of different issues. Should the crime be recorded if it is the focus of the news report, even though all they see is the ambulance leaving the scene? Should it be recorded if no one is sure how many people died? In order to look carefully at the profile of the news, your students may find that they need to have different definitions for the news stories.

Your students can make their own decisions about whether they will include the news coverage in their research. Some of them may want to analyze the newspaper and radio coverage as well—older students, especially, are interested in how real life is represented in the media. Television news is supposed to represent real-life stories, and if

those do not seem to match reality, students may raise some important questions.

If your class spends further time analyzing the media, there are some interesting questions to explore. Are the media all alike? Do newspapers differ in the amount and kind of crime they report? Do "all-day news" TV and radio stations differ from those that report the news for short periods of time?

These and other questions need to be discussed at some length before your students begin data collection. ■

Data sheet: Incidence of crimes by state

The table below lists crimes by state and by type per 100,000 population. Figures given are for 1987. This material is adapted from the U.S. Bureau of the Census, *Statistical Abstract of the United States: 1989* (109th edition), page 166.

If you are unable to locate more current data, find your state in the table and provide your class with these statistics for comparison with the data for the country as a whole (Student Sheets 5 and 6) and with the data they collect about TV crime.

Division and state	Murder	Robbery	Aggravated Assault	Burglary	Larceny/ Theft	Motor Vehicle Theft
Northeast	**3.4**	**139**	**252**	**1074**	**2447**	**656**
ME	2.5	26	108	771	2436	173
NH	3.0	26	93	695	2311	216
VT	2.7	17	95	1110	2826	199
MA	3.0	177	353	1060	2185	924
RI	3.5	108	224	1441	2701	783
CT	4.9	178	211	1218	2829	529
Mid-Atlantic	**8.0**	**333**	**337**	**1016**	**2577**	**619**
NY	11.3	503	462	1216	3025	703
NJ	4.6	233	270	1009	2866	845
PA	5.4	144	193	722	1723	349
E. North Central	**7.6**	**206**	**316**	**1124**	**2930**	**488**
OH	5.8	153	222	1063	2709	383
IN	5.6	89	205	947	2490	355
IL	8.3	314	435	1124	2957	540
MI	12.2	277	424	1452	3473	752
WI	3.5	66	160	843	2830	247
W. North Central	**4.4**	**95**	**219**	**1002**	**2792**	**279**
MN	2.6	103	146	1069	2960	301
IA	2.1	36	181	918	2840	151
MO	8.3	164	343	1111	2625	426
ND	1.5	8	38	455	2198	123
SD	1.8	12	85	534	1928	96
NE	3.5	47	179	848	2866	166
KS	4.4	82	242	1138	3152	253

Division and state	Murder	Robbery	Aggravated Assault	Burglary	Larceny/ Theft	Motor Vehicle Theft
South Atlantic	**10.0**	**217**	**406**	**1514**	**3276**	**453**
DE	5.1	123	235	1020	3176	312
MD	9.6	290	428	1162	2965	582
DC	36.2	717	817	1808	4021	1012
VA	7.4	106	156	807	2603	254
WV	4.8	31	79	604	1288	162
NC	8.1	94	353	1356	2586	224
SC	9.3	101	511	1358	2858	281
GA	11.8	209	312	1552	3171	492
FL	11.4	357	606	2257	4545	677
E. South Central	**9.0**	**123**	**284**	**1162**	**2124**	**325**
KY	7.5	90	219	847	1892	193
TN	9.1	194	287	1352	2213	567
AL	9.3	112	410	1198	2431	263
MS	10.2	57	173	1201	1807	160
W. South Central	**10.7**	**191**	**351**	**1873**	**3813**	**619**
AR	7.6	79	293	1078	2549	207
LA	11.1	179	467	1445	3323	413
OK	7.5	110	265	1783	3220	605
TX	11.7	227	345	2118	4238	735
Mountain	**6.2**	**109**	**312**	**1402**	**3935**	**359**
MT	4.1	24	103	806	3403	238
ID	3.1	24	169	977	2798	167
WY	2.0	20	230	718	2892	139
CO	5.8	119	302	1535	4013	436
NM	10.1	108	467	1788	3785	346
AZ	7.5	138	425	1626	4527	423
UT	3.3	53	152	951	4228	209
NV	8.4	272	353	1629	3491	555
Pacific	**9.4**	**264**	**486**	**1567**	**3466**	**730**
WA	5.6	141	240	1905	4278	395
OR	5.6	196	292	1783	4182	465
CA	10.6	301	562	1518	3240	830
AK	10.1	73	307	970	3466	486
HI	4.8	98	124	1156	4033	366

Ask these questions in your small group. From your results, predict what you think will be true for the whole class.

1. Do you have a pet?
   Group results: _____
   Class prediction: _____
   _____

2. When do you usually go to bed on weeknights?
   Group results: _____
   Class prediction: _____
   _____

3. Do you have a little sister?
   Group results: _____
   Class prediction: _____
   _____

4. Have you ever gone fishing?
   Group results: _____
   Class prediction: _____
   _____

GETTING MORE FAMILY DATA

Use this sheet to keep track of the new family-size data you are collecting.

Copy the definition of a family here:

_____

_____

_____

Keep track of your results below.

Family Identifier	Family Size		Family Identifier	Family Size

Cat's name		
Gender	Age (years)	Weight (pounds)
Body length (inches)	Tail length (inches)	
Fur color	Eye color	Pad color
Other		

When you write in your data for the cat you choose, you can make comments about the cat after the heading "Other."

BROWSING IN THE DATA BASE

To FIND data . . .

You can set up your data base to FIND specific information. If you want to see all the cats with pink pads, select FIND from the menu and then select (or type in) PADS and then select (or type in) PINK. The computer will instantly find those records and put them on top of the pile. You can then SCAN the records and pick them out easily.

To practice finding information, use the data base to answer these questions.

- How many cats have black fur?
- How many cats have green eyes?

To ORDER data . . .

If you want to put the cats in order by some characteristic, you can ask the computer to ORDER—meaning to put the data in order. Usually, the program then requests that you tell it *how* to ORDER the data. Lowest to highest numbers or A to Z are typical ways of ordering.

To practice ordering, use the data base to answer these questions.

- Which cat is heaviest?
- Which is the last cat if the names are in alphabetical order?
- How many cats are older than you?

Other situations . . .

Sometimes you have to figure out what to do yourself, because it's complicated. Try using the data base to answer this question:

- Which cats are both old and fairly heavy?

Make up some of your own problems, and share them with your group.

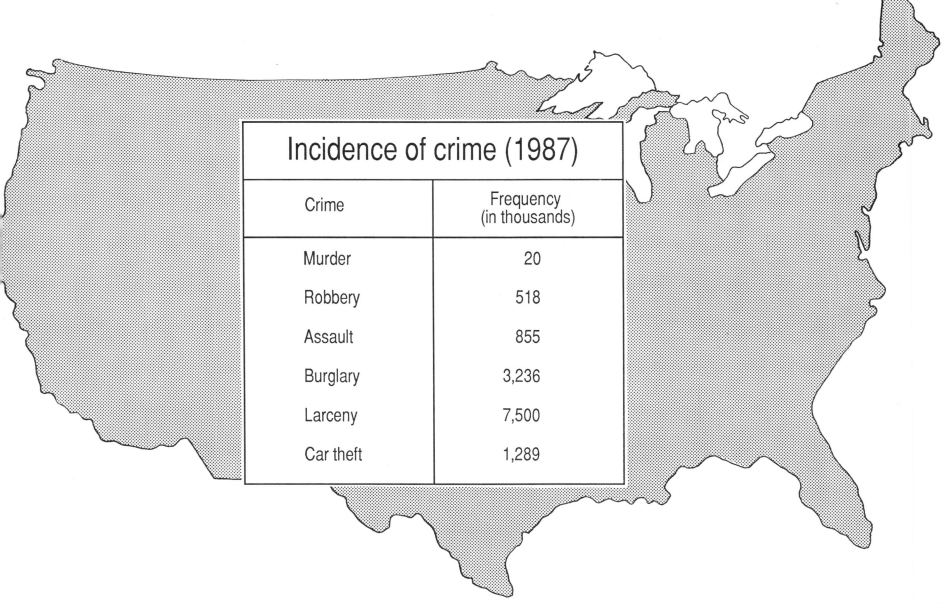

Incidence of crime (1987)

Crime	Frequency (in thousands)
Murder	20
Robbery	518
Assault	855
Burglary	3,236
Larceny	7,500
Car theft	1,289

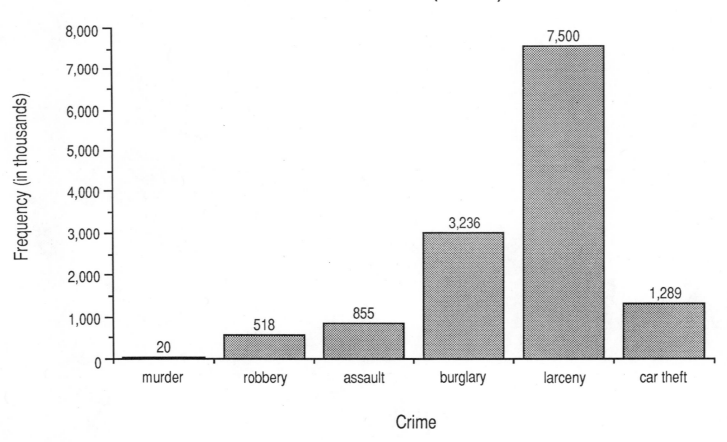

Incidence of crime (1987)

Name of the show: _____

Length of the show: _____

Channel: _____

Date: _____

Crime	Observations
Murder	
Robbery	
Assault	
Burglary	
Larceny	
Car theft	
Other crimes	

CAT CARDS

The 24 cat pictures and data on the following pages are for use with the investigation *Cats: Sampling a population of animals.* For a single set of cards that can be shared among small groups of students, remove the 12 pages, cut them in two, and mount or laminate each card for durability.

Because it is most convenient if each small group has its own set of cat cards, you may want to try duplicating these pages. The quality of the duplicated pictures will vary, depending on your copier. If possible, duplicate them on card stock.

A full-color version of the cat photos is available from Dale Seymour Publications as a large poster, with the cat data printed on the back of each picture. You can cut apart this poster and laminate the individual photos or place each one in a transparent sleeve to create an attractive set of cat cards with lots of student appeal.

Lady Jane Grey

Gender: female
Age: 4 years
Weight: 8.5 pounds

Body length: 19 inches
Tail length: 11 inches
Fur color: gray
Eye color: yellow
Pad color: gray
Other:

Peau de Soie

Gender: female
Age: 15 years
Weight: 7 pounds

Body length: 16 inches
Tail length: 13 inches
Fur color: orange, black, and white
Eye color: green
Pad color: pink
Other: Peau de Soie means "skin of silk" in French; her
               nickname is Peau (rhymes with *go*).

Mittens

Gender:	female
Age:	14 years
Weight:	10.5 pounds
Body length:	17 inches
Tail length:	11 inches
Fur color:	orange and white
Eye color:	yellow
Pad color:	pink
Other:	Mittens has six toes on each foot.

Tigger

Gender:	female
Age:	4 years
Weight:	8 pounds
Body length:	17 inches
Tail length:	10 inches
Fur color:	orange, black, and white
Eye color:	yellow
Pad color:	brown
Other:	

Weary

Gender:	male
Age:	8 years
Weight:	15 pounds
Body length:	17 inches
Tail length:	12 inches
Fur color:	black and white
Eye color:	green
Pad color:	pink
Other:	

Ravena

Gender:	female
Age:	6 years
Weight:	14 pounds
Body length:	23 inches
Tail length:	12 inches
Fur color:	orange, black, gold, and white
Eye color:	yellow
Pad color:	pink and black
Other:	

Lady

Gender: female
Age: 10 years
Weight: 8.5 pounds

Body length: 17 inches
Tail length: 13 inches
Fur color: gray, brown, and white stripes
Eye color: yellow
Pad color: black
Other:

Wally

Gender: male
Age: 5 years
Weight: 10 pounds

Body length: 18 inches
Tail length: 12 inches
Fur color: black and white
Eye color: green
Pad color: pink and black
Other: Wally is Peeble's brother.

Peebles

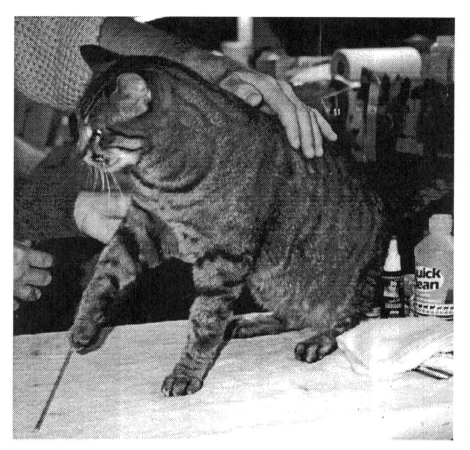

K.C.

Gender:	female
Age:	5 years
Weight:	9 pounds
Body length:	17 inches
Tail length:	11 inches
Fur color:	gray
Eye color:	green
Pad color:	black
Other:	Peebles is Wally's sister.

Gender:	male
Age:	5 years
Weight:	16 pounds
Body length:	24 inches
Tail length:	12 inches
Fur color:	brown and black stripes, some white
Eye color:	yellow
Pad color:	black
Other:	

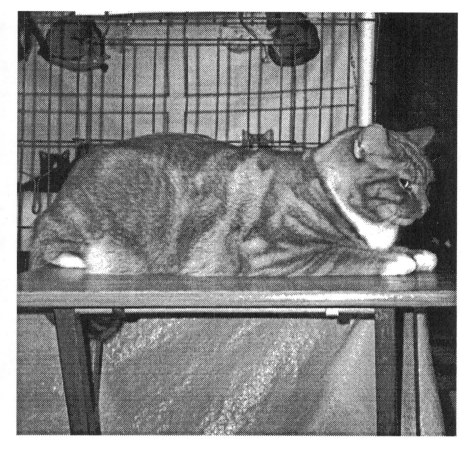

Oddfuzz

Gender:	male
Age:	5 years
Weight:	18 pounds
Body length:	21 inches
Tail length:	9 inches
Fur color:	orange and white
Eye color:	yellow
Pad color:	pink
Other:	

Melissa

Gender:	female
Age:	8 years
Weight:	11 pounds
Body length:	21 inches
Tail length:	11 inches
Fur color:	white, black, and orange
Eye color:	yellow
Pad color:	pink
Other:	

Pepper

Gender:	male
Age:	2 years
Weight:	12 pounds
Body length:	17 inches
Tail length:	9 inches
Fur color:	orange
Eye color:	yellow
Pad color:	pink
Other:	Pepper was known as an escape artist at the animal shelter where he was living.

Strawberry

Gender:	female
Age:	16 years
Weight:	14.5 pounds
Body length:	21 inches
Tail length:	10 inches
Fur color:	gray, brown, and white stripes
Eye color:	green
Pad color:	black
Other:	

Alexander

Gender:	male
Age:	18 years
Weight:	11 pounds
Body length:	21 inches
Tail length:	11 inches
Fur color:	brown and black stripes, some white
Eye color:	green
Pad color:	black
Other:	Alex's favorite foods are vanilla ice cream and bacon, which he will steal off the table.

Misty

Gender:	male
Age:	1 year
Weight:	9 pounds
Body length:	18 inches
Tail length:	11 inches
Fur color:	gray, white, and black
Eye color:	green
Pad color:	pink and black
Other:	

George

Diva

Gender:	male
Age:	12 years
Weight:	14.5 pounds

Body length:	21 inches
Tail length:	13 inches
Fur color:	black and white
Eye color:	green
Pad color:	black
Other:	

Gender:	female
Age:	3.5 years
Weight:	11 pounds

Body length:	20 inches
Tail length:	12 inches
Fur color:	gray, black, brown stripes with white patches
Eye color:	green
Pad color:	pink
Other:	

Gray Kitty

Gender:	female
Age:	3 years
Weight:	9 pounds
Body length:	15 inches
Tail length:	8.5 inches
Fur color:	gray
Eye color:	green
Pad color:	gray
Other:	Gray Kitty was living at an animal shelter.

Tomodachi Joto

Gender:	male
Age:	1 year
Weight:	6.5 pounds
Body length:	14 inches
Tail length:	1.5 inches
Fur color:	white and red
Eye color:	gold
Pad color:	pink
Other:	Tomodachi Joto means "best friend" in Japanese. Nicknamed Joto, he is a Japanese bobtail cat.

Harmony

Gender:	male
Age:	3 years
Weight:	12 pounds
Body length:	24 inches
Tail length:	11 inches
Fur color:	black
Eye color:	greenish gold
Pad color:	black
Other:	

Augustus

Gender:	male
Age:	2 years
Weight:	10 pounds
Body length:	21 inches
Tail length:	11 inches
Fur color:	black and white
Eye color:	yellow, green, blue
Pad color:	pink and black
Other:	Augustus, Gus for short, is a long-haired cat. He was found as a stray.

Charcoal

Gender:	male
Age:	11 years
Weight:	12 pounds
Body length:	21 inches
Tail length:	13 inches
Fur color:	black and white
Eye color:	yellow
Pad color:	black
Other:	Charcoal has big feet.

Cleopatra

Gender:	female
Age:	4 years
Weight:	7 pounds
Body length:	18 inches
Tail length:	9 inches
Fur color:	black
Eye color:	golden green
Pad color:	pink
Other:	

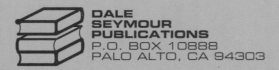

DALE SEYMOUR PUBLICATIONS
P.O. BOX 10888
PALO ALTO, CA 94303

Dale Seymour Publications is a leading publisher of K–12 supplementary materials in mathematics, thinking skills, science, language arts, and art education

Used Numbers: Real Data in the Classroom

A project of Technical Education Research Centers (TERC), Lesley College, and the Consortium for Mathematics and Its Applications (COMAP)

These six units of study, extensively field-tested, teach elementary and middle school students how to collect and analyze real-world data. Each book offers a series of investigations that can be completed in about 15 class sessions with lots of hands-on activities, small-group work, and team problem solving.

Counting: Ourselves and Our Families	Grades K–1
Sorting: Groups and Graphs	Grades 2–3
Measuring: From Paces to Feet	Grades 3–4
Statistics: The Shape of the Data	Grades 4–6
Statistics: Prediction and Sampling	Grades 5–6
Statistics: Middles, Means, and In-Betweens	Grades 5–6

9 780866 515160

90000 >

ISBN 0-86651-516-X
01037